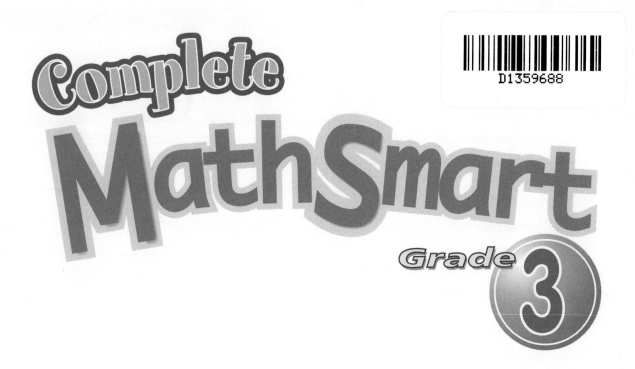

D1359688

Consultant: Ann Bobker

Contents

Section 1

Overview

In Grade 2, children developed arithmetic skills which included addition and subtraction up to 100 as well as writing and ordering 2-digit and 3-digit numbers.

In this section, children develop these skills further to include ordering, and adding and subtracting 4-digit numbers. Multiplication of 1-digit numbers and division of 2-digit numbers by 1-digit numbers are introduced and practised. The concepts of Fraction and Decimal are also explained.

Money applications include the use of decimals and sums up to $10. Measurement skills are expanded to include standard units for recording perimeter, area, capacity, volume and mass.

Organizing data and constructing pictographs and bar graphs are practised. Children are also encouraged to use mathematical language to discuss probability.

4-digit Numbers

Write the numbers. Then put the numbers in order.

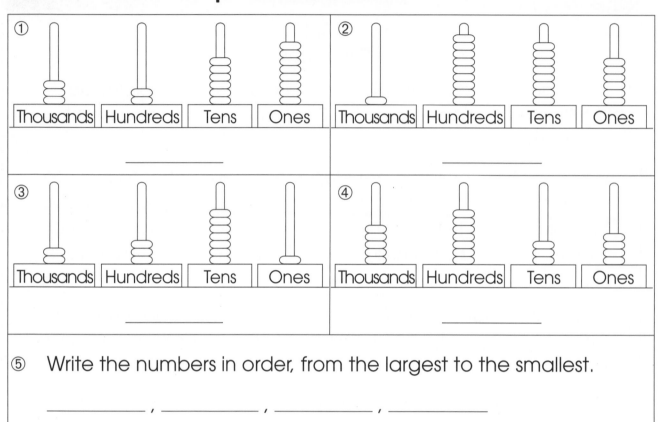

① Thousands | Hundreds | Tens | Ones

_____

② Thousands | Hundreds | Tens | Ones

_____

③ Thousands | Hundreds | Tens | Ones

_____

④ Thousands | Hundreds | Tens | Ones

_____

⑤ Write the numbers in order, from the largest to the smallest.

_____ , _____ , _____ , _____

Write the numbers or words.

⑥ The largest 4-digit number with 5, 6, 1 and 4   _____

⑦ The smallest 4-digit number with 3, 0, 8 and 6   _____

⑧ The largest 4-digit odd number with 5, 9, 2 and 3   _____

⑨ The smallest 4-digit even number with 1, 7, 4 and 2   _____

⑩ The number 2341 in words   _____

⑪ The number 4102 in words   _____

⑫ The number 7009 in words   _____

Riverview School is collecting pennies for a local hospital. See how many pennies each jar can hold. Then answer the questions.

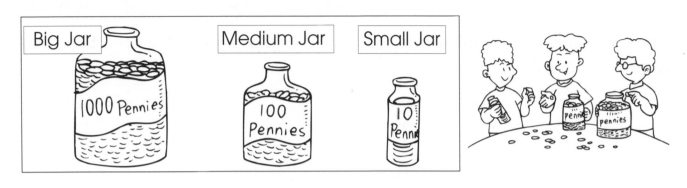

⑬ Grade 1 fill 1 big jar and 2 medium jars. How many pennies do they collect?

1000 + 100 + 100

_____ pennies

⑭ Grade 2 fill 2 big jars and 5 small jars. How many pennies do they collect?

1000 + 1000 + 10 + 10 + 10 + 10 + 10

_____ pennies

⑮ Grade 3 fill 3 big jars and 4 medium jars. How many pennies do they collect?

_____ pennies

⑯ Grade 4 fill 2 big jars, 2 small jars and collect 5 more pennies. How many pennies do they collect?

_____ pennies

⑰ Grade 5 collect 3000 pennies. How many big jars do they fill?

_____ big jars

⑱ Grade 6 collect 900 pennies. How many medium jars do they fill?

_____ medium jars

⑲ Which grade collects the most pennies?

Grade _____

⑳ 9380 pennies are collected. How many jars of different sizes can be filled, using the fewest jars?

Addition and Subtraction

The table shows the number of students in 5 high schools. Read the table and answer the questions.

	Allentown School	Brownsville School	Cedarbrae School	Davisville School	Eagletown School
Number of students	1050	1025	1330	1040	1245

① Which school has the largest number of students?

_____

② Which school has the smallest number of students?

_____

③ 426 students in Allentown School are girls. How many boys are in Allentown School?

_____ = _____   _____ boys

④ 50 students are transferred from Brownsville School to Cedarbrae School. How many students are now at Brownsville School?

_____ = _____   _____ students

⑤ How many students are now at Cedarbrae School?

_____ = _____   _____ students

⑥ 250 students of Davisville School go to school by bus. How many students of the school do not go to school by bus?

_____ = _____   _____ students

⑦ 319 students of Eagletown School wear glasses. How many students of the school do not wear glasses?

_____ = _____   _____ students

Uncle William recorded the number of sandwiches and pitas sold last month. Look at his record and answer the questions.

	Roast Beef	Chicken Salad	Turkey Breast
Sandwich	582	394	1325
Pita	1429	1066	849

⑧ How many roast beef sandwiches and pitas were sold?

_____ = _____

_____ roast beef sandwiches and pitas were sold.

⑨ How many chicken salad sandwiches and pitas were sold?

_____ = _____

_____ chicken salad sandwiches and pitas were sold.

⑩ How many turkey breast sandwiches and pitas were sold?

_____ = _____

_____ turkey breast sandwiches and pitas were sold.

⑪ How many sandwiches were sold?

_____ = _____

_____ sandwiches were sold.

⑫ How many pitas were sold?

_____ = _____

_____ pitas were sold.

⑬ How many fewer sandwiches than pitas were sold?

_____ = _____

_____ fewer sandwiches than pitas were sold.

Find the sums or differences. Match the letters with the answers to see what Charlie says.

⑭ 1234 + 2345 /g	⑮ 4800 − 1200 /h	⑯ 5360 − 1250 /n
⑰ 2317 + 2503 /f	⑱ 2425 + 1293 /u	⑲ 5000 − 1200 /i
⑳ 2600 − 1580 /h	㉑ 2367 + 1425 /a	㉒ 965 + 3279 /p
㉓ 5123 − 1354 /u	㉔ 4014 − 3122 /k	㉕ 1456 + 399 /b
㉖ 4444 − 1666 /c	㉗ 2008 + 1994 /s	㉘ 3000 − 561 /d
㉙ 2463 + 558 /t	㉚ 3246 − 1268 /l	㉛ 889 + 255 /s

㉜

M ＿＿ ＿＿ ＿＿ ＿＿ ＿＿ ＿＿ ＿＿ ＿＿ ＿＿
    3792 3021 1020   3800 4002   1144 3718 2778 3600

＿＿ ＿＿ ＿＿ !
4820 3769 4110

The Smart Girls performed in 4 cities last year. The table shows the attendance at each of their concerts. Look at the table and answer the questions.

City	Attendance
Toronto	3590
Montreal	2945
Calgary	1782
Vancouver	2595

㉝ How many people in total attended the concert in Toronto or Montreal?

_____ = _____   _____ people

㉞ How many people in total attended the concert in Calgary or Vancouver?

_____ = _____   _____ people

㉟ How many more people attended the concert in Vancouver than in Calgary?

_____ = _____   _____ more people

㊱ 1827 girls attended the concert in Montreal. How many boys attended that concert?

_____ = _____   _____ boys

㊲ The band expects to have 260 more people attending their concert in Toronto this year. How many people are expected?

_____ = _____   _____ people

㊳ The band expects to have 290 fewer people attending their concert in Calgary this year. How many people are expected?

_____ = _____   _____ people

③ Multiplication

Count and write the number of pictures on the cards to complete the tables. Then fill in the blanks.

①

a.	Number of cards	1	2	3	4	5	6
	Total number of ♡						

b. There are _____ threes.　　　c. _____ x 3 = _____

②

a.	Number of cards	1	2	3	4	5	6	7
	Total number of ☆							

b. There are _____ fours.　　　c. _____ x 4 = _____

③

a.	Number of cards	1	2	3	4	5	6
	Total number of △						

b. There are _____ eights.　　　c. _____ x 8 = _____

④

a.	Number of cards	1	2	3	4	5
	Total number of ♔					

b. There are _____ sevens.　　　c. _____ x 7 = _____

⑤

a.	Number of cards	1	2	3	4	5	6	7	8
	Total number of ✄								

b. There are _____ twos.　　　c. _____ x 2 = _____

Count the number of animals in each picture. Then check ✔ the correct answers and fill in the blanks.

⑥

Ⓐ 3 x 7　　Ⓑ 6 x 3

Ⓒ 6 fours　Ⓓ 6 threes

There are _____ rabbits.

⑦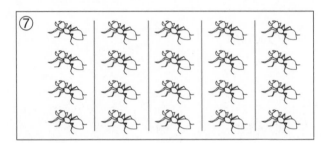

Ⓐ 4 fours　Ⓑ 5 fours

Ⓒ 5 x 4　　Ⓓ 5 x 5

There are _____ ants.

⑧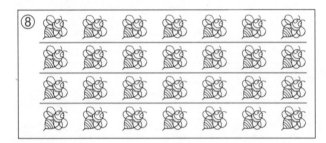

Ⓐ 4 sevens　Ⓑ 4 sixes

Ⓒ 6 x 4　　Ⓓ 4 x 7

There are _____ bees.

⑨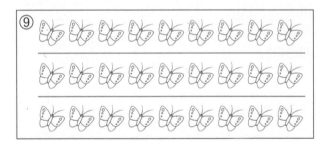

Ⓐ 9 x 4　　Ⓑ 3 nines

Ⓒ 4 nines　Ⓓ 3 x 9

There are _____ butterflies.

⑩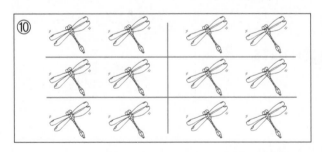

Ⓐ 6 twos　　Ⓑ 6 x 2

Ⓒ 6 threes　Ⓓ 3 x 6

There are _____ dragonflies.

⑪

Ⓐ 4 x 5　　Ⓑ 4 x 6

Ⓒ 4 sixes　Ⓓ 5 x 6

There are _____ beetles.

Look at the pictures. Then write the numbers to complete each sentence.

⑫ a. Each cat has _____ whiskers. 8 cats have _____ whiskers.

    b. Each cat has _____ eyes. 8 cats have _____ eyes.

⑬ a. Each flower has _____ leaves. 9 flowers have _____ leaves.

    b. Each flower has _____ petals. 9 flowers have _____ petals.

⑭ a. Each bracelet has _____ big beads. 6 bracelets have _____ big beads.

    b. Each bracelet has _____ small beads. 6 bracelets have _____ small beads.

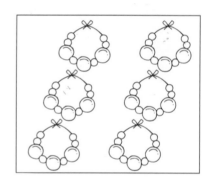

⑮ a. Each tray holds _____ cakes. 3 trays hold _____ cakes.

    b. Each tray holds _____ doughnuts. 3 trays hold _____ doughnuts.

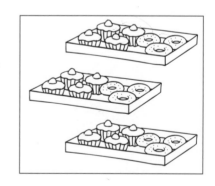

⑯ a. Each dog has _____ legs. 7 dogs have _____ legs.

    b. Each dog has _____ ears. 7 dogs have _____ ears.

See what Adam takes when he goes camping. Help him solve the problems.

⑰ A box holds 6 eggs. How many eggs are there in 3 boxes?

_____ x _____ = _____

There are _____ eggs in 3 boxes.

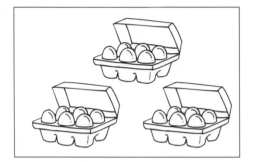

⑱ A pack has 8 sausages. How many sausages are there in 4 packs?

_____ x _____ = _____

There are _____ sausages in 4 packs.

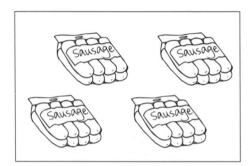

⑲ A bag has 5 buns. How many buns are there in 5 bags?

_____ x _____ = _____

There are _____ buns in 5 bags.

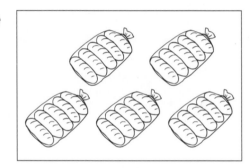

⑳ A pack has 8 batteries. How many batteries are there in 7 packs?

_____ x _____ = _____

There are _____ batteries in 7 packs.

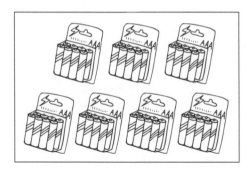

㉑ A bunch has 9 bananas. How many bananas are there in 5 bunches?

_____ x _____ = _____

There are _____ bananas in 5 bunches.

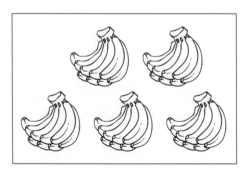

 **Division**

Look at the pictures. Write the numbers.

①

a. There are _____ groups of 5 in 15.

b. 15 ÷ 5 = _____

②

a. There are _____ groups of 9 in 18.

b. 18 ÷ 9 = _____

③

a. There are _____ groups of 3 in 12.

b. 12 ÷ 3 = _____

④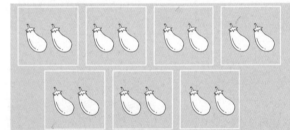

a. There are _____ groups of 2 in 14.

b. 14 ÷ 2 = _____

⑤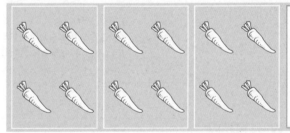

a. There are _____ groups of 4 in 12.

b. 12 ÷ 4 = _____

⑥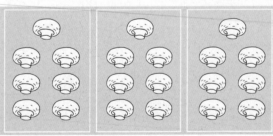

a. There are _____ groups of 7 in 21.

b. 21 ÷ 7 = _____

See how the children divide their stickers. Help them circle each group of stickers and write the numbers.

⑦ Wayne divides 18 stickers into 2 equal groups.

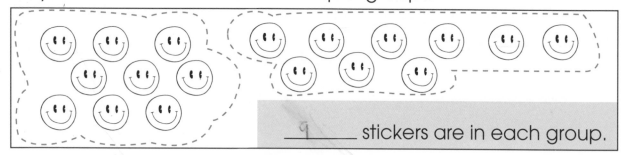

_____9_____ stickers are in each group.

⑧ Ivy divides 15 stickers into 5 equal groups.

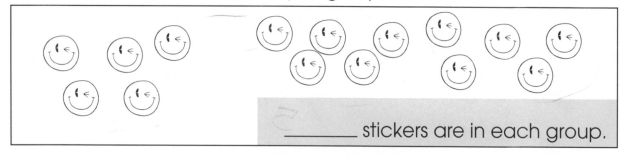

_____ stickers are in each group.

⑨ Matthew divides 20 stickers into 4 equal groups.

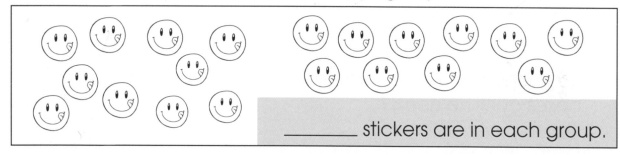

_____ stickers are in each group.

⑩ Joe divides 21 stickers into 3 equal groups.

_____ stickers are in each group.

⑪ Louis divides 16 stickers into 4 equal groups.

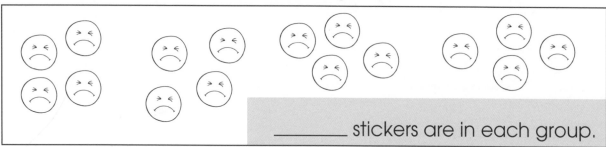

_____ stickers are in each group.

Raymond puts his stationery into boxes. Help him circle each group of stationery and write the numbers.

⑫ Raymond has 24 pencils. He puts 6 pencils into each box. How many boxes does he need?

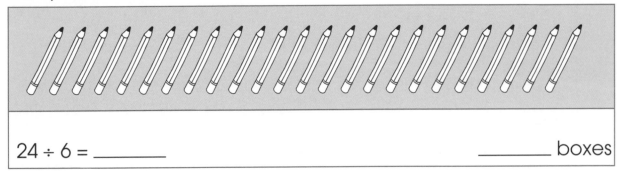

24 ÷ 6 = _____   _____ boxes

⑬ Raymond has 28 crayons. He puts 4 crayons into each box. How many boxes does he need?

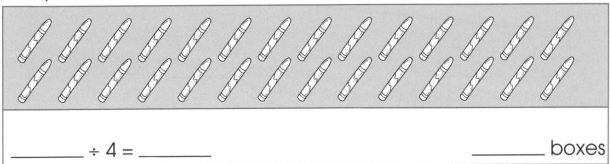

_____ ÷ 4 = _____   _____ boxes

⑭ Raymond has 30 pens. He puts 5 pens into each box. How many boxes does he need?

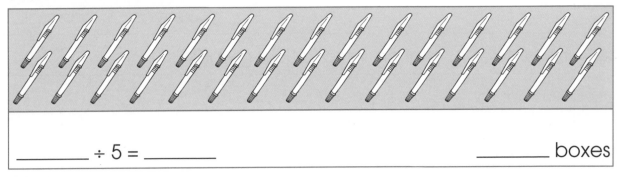

_____ ÷ 5 = _____   _____ boxes

⑮ Raymond has 40 markers. He puts 8 markers into each box. How many boxes does he need?

_____ ÷ 8 = _____   _____ boxes

Answer the questions.

⑯ Put 18 cookies into 6 jars. How many cookies are there in each jar?

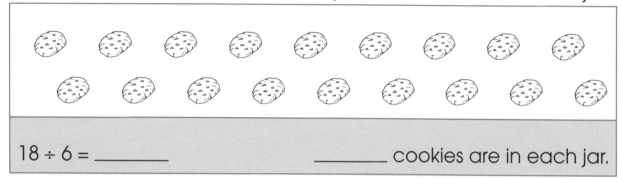

18 ÷ 6 = _____   _____ cookies are in each jar.

⑰ Put 24 muffins into 4 boxes. How many muffins are there in each box?

_____ ÷ 4 = _____   _____ muffins are in each box.

⑱ Put 26 doughnuts into 3 bags. How many doughnuts are there in each bag?   How many doughnuts are left over?

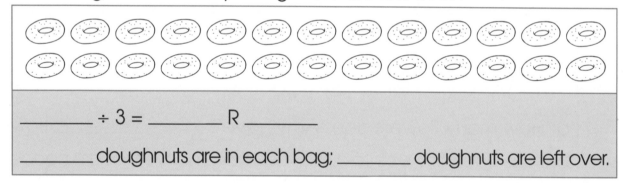

_____ ÷ 3 = _____ R _____

_____ doughnuts are in each bag; _____ doughnuts are left over.

⑲ Put 23 pretzels into 5 baskets. How many pretzels are there in each basket? How many pretzels are left over?

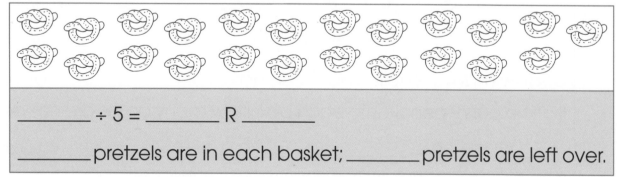

_____ ÷ 5 = _____ R _____

_____ pretzels are in each basket; _____ pretzels are left over.

5 More about Multiplication and Division

See what the children have. Help them solve the problems.

①

a. Nancy has _____ plates of cookies; each plate has _____ cookies.

b. How many cookies are there in all?

_____ x 8 = _____   _____ cookies

②

a. Julia has _____ baskets of apples; each basket has _____ apples.

b. How many apples are there in all?

_____ x 7 = _____   _____ apples

③

a. How many flowers does Amy have?   _____ flowers

b. If she puts 5 flowers into each vase, how many vases are needed?

_____ ÷ 5 = _____   _____ vases

④

a. How many pencils does Brian have?   _____ pencils

b. If he puts 9 pencils into each box, how many boxes are needed?

_____ ÷ 9 = _____   _____ boxes

Answer the questions.

⑤ Jim cuts a pizza into 8 slices. If he gets 48 slices, how many pizzas has he cut?

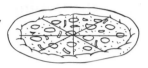

_____ ÷ _____ = _____   _____ pizzas

⑥ Ivan has 3 bags of marbles. Each bag contains 9 marbles. How many marbles does Ivan have?

_____ x _____ = _____   _____ marbles

⑦ Each page of a photo album has 3 photos. How many photos are there on 8 pages?

_____ x _____ = _____   _____ photos

⑧ Each box holds 4 muffins. How many boxes are needed to hold 36 muffins?

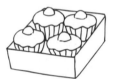

_____ ÷ _____ = _____   _____ boxes

⑨ Each child has 7 pennies. How many pennies do 6 children have?

_____ x _____ = _____   _____ pennies

⑩ Joe has 25 baseball cards. He puts 5 cards into a pile. How many piles can he get?

_____ ÷ _____ = _____   _____ piles

⑪ A pack has 6 stickers. How many stickers are there in 3 packs?

_____ x _____ = _____   _____ stickers

Midway | Review

Fill in the missing numbers.

①   1169, 1170, _____ , _____ , 1173, _____ , 1175

②   2588, 2688, _____ , _____ , 2988, _____ , 3188

③   9214, _____ , 7214, _____ , 5214, _____ , 3214

④   4016, _____ , 4012, _____ , 4008, _____ , 4004

Use the following numbers to answer the questions.

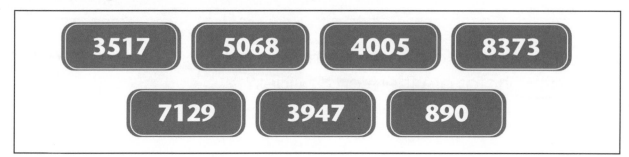

⑤   How many numbers are bigger than 5000?   _____

⑥   Which number is smaller than 4000 but bigger than 3600?   _____

⑦   Which number has 5 in its thousands place?   _____

⑧   Which number has 3 in its hundreds place?   _____

⑨   How many even numbers are there?   _____

⑩   What is the sum of the smallest and the biggest numbers?   _____

⑪   What is the difference between the smallest and the biggest numbers?   _____

⑫   Write the biggest number in words.

_____

⑬   Write the smallest number in words.

_____

The table shows how many stamps each child has. Help the children fill in the boxes on the number line and answer the questions.

	Eva	Molly	Brad	Mary	George
Number of stamps	927	2018	1806	1446	1129

⑭ Put the names and numbers in the boxes to show how many stamps each child has.

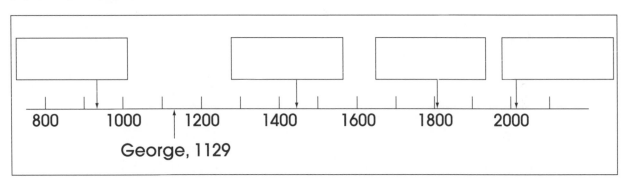

George, 1129

⑮ How many stamps do Eva and Molly have?

_____ = _____   _____ stamps

⑯ How many more stamps does Molly have than Eva?

_____ = _____   _____ more stamps

⑰ How many stamps do Brad and Mary have?

_____ = _____   _____ stamps

⑱ How many fewer stamps does Mary have than Brad?

_____ = _____   _____ fewer stamps

⑲ How many stamps do the boys have?

_____ = _____   _____ stamps

⑳ How many stamps do the girls have?

_____ = _____   _____ stamps

Answer the questions.

㉑

a. Each tricycle has 3 wheels. How many wheels are there in 6 tricycles?

_____ x 3 = _____   _____ wheels

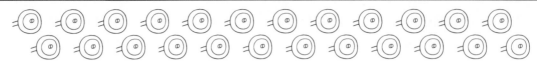

b. How many tricycles can be fitted with 24 wheels?

_____ ÷ 3 = _____   _____ tricycles

㉒

a. Each pincushion has 7 pins. How many pins are there in 5 pincushions?

_____ x 7 = _____   _____ pins

b. How many pincushions are needed to hold 28 pins?

_____ ÷ 7 = _____   _____ pincushions

㉓

a. Each tray holds 9 cakes. How many cakes are there on 3 trays?

_____ x 9 = _____   _____ cakes

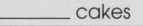

b. How many trays are needed to hold 18 cakes?

_____ ÷ 9 = _____   _____ trays

Look at the pictures. Write the numbers.

㉔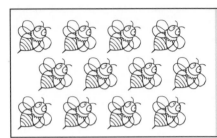
a. 3 x 4 = _____   b. 2 x 6 = _____

c. 12 ÷ 3 = _____   d. 12 ÷ 2 = _____

㉕
a. 2 x 9 = _____   b. 3 x 6 = _____

c. 18 ÷ 2 = _____   d. 18 ÷ 6 = _____

㉖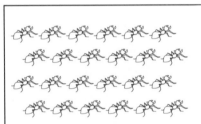
a. 3 x 8 = _____   b. 6 x 4 = _____

c. 24 ÷ 8 = _____   d. 24 ÷ 6 = _____

Answer the questions.

㉗ 8 flowers are divided into 2 equal groups. How many flowers are there in each group?

_____ ÷ 2 = _____   _____ flowers

㉘ Each box holds 6 sandwiches. How many sandwiches are there in 9 boxes?

_____ x 6 = _____   _____ sandwiches

㉙ Mrs Feler divides 63 markers equally among 7 children. How many markers can each child get?

_____ ÷ 7 = _____   _____ markers

㉚ Each row has 9 chairs. How many chairs are there in 4 rows?

_____ x 9 = _____   _____ chairs

Measurement

Circle the correct answers.

① Which is a better unit for measuring the length of a dining table?

② Which is a better unit for measuring the weight of an apple?

③ Which is a better unit for measuring the length of a football field?   centimetre   metre

④ Which is a better unit for measuring the time you sleep every night?   second   hour

⑤ Which is a better unit for measuring the time you take to brush your teeth?   minute   hour

⑥ How many minutes are there in 1 hour?   30   60

⑦ How many hours are there in 1 day?   24   25

Find the perimeter of each shape.

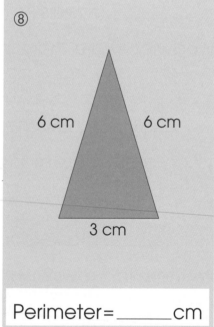

⑧

6 cm   6 cm

3 cm

Perimeter = _____ cm

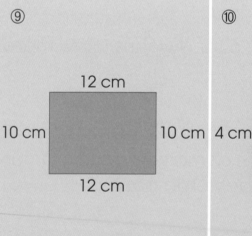

⑨

12 cm

10 cm   10 cm

12 cm

Perimeter = _____ cm

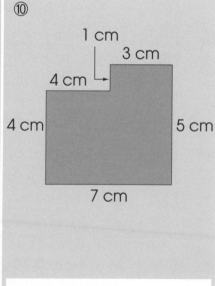

⑩

1 cm

3 cm

4 cm

4 cm   5 cm

7 cm

Perimeter = _____ cm

Mrs Ling wants to bake a cake. Look at the ingredients, times and temperatures. Answer the questions.

⑪ Which ingredient is the heaviest? _____

⑫ Which ingredient is the lightest? _____

⑬ Which is heavier, the sugar or the cocoa? _____

⑭ Draw the hands on the clock faces to show the time Mrs Ling starts to bake her cake and the time the cake is done.

a. Start 12:45 p.m.

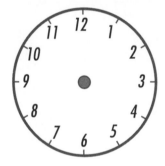

b. Finish 2:15 p.m.

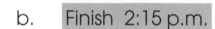

⑮ How long did it take to bake the cake? _____

⑯ Write the temperatures in the kitchen and in the living room.

a.

kitchen

_____ ˚C

b.

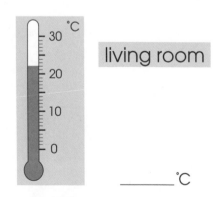

living room

_____ ˚C

⑰ Which place has a higher temperature, the kitchen or the living room? _____

Money

Check ✔ the correct number of coins to pay for each toy in 2 different ways.

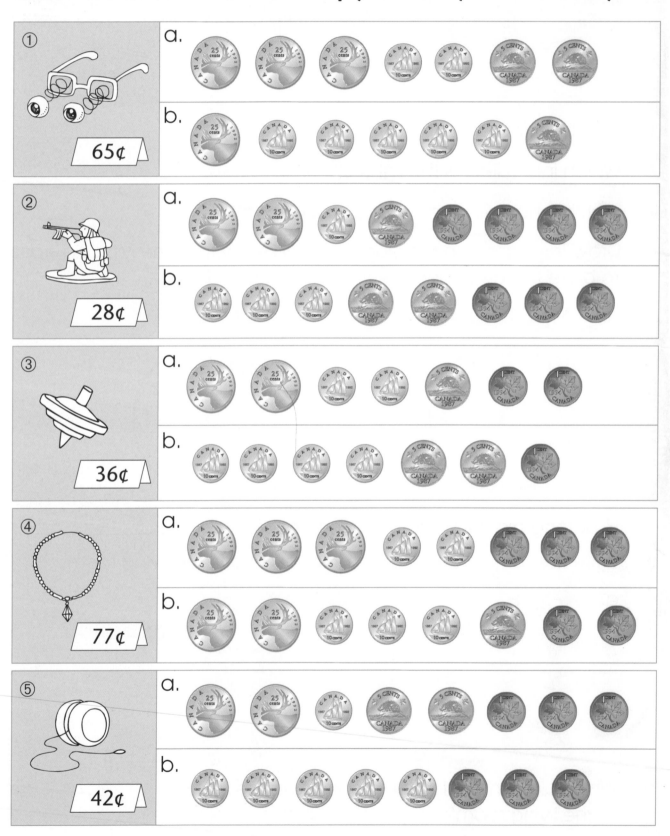

Write how much money each child has. Then see what they buy and write how much they have left.

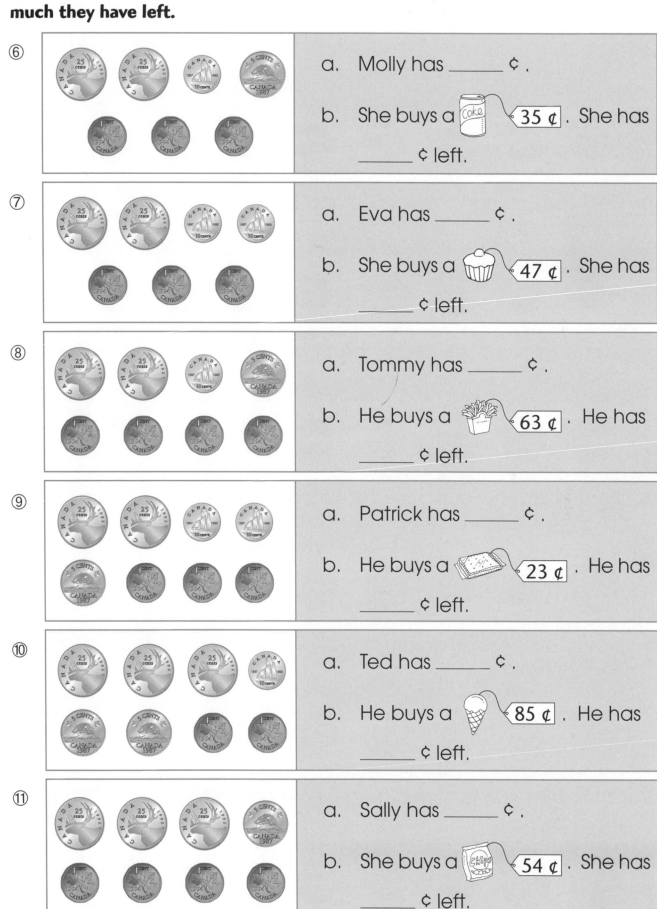

6. a. Molly has _____ ¢ .

    b. She buys a ![Coke] ⟨ 35 ¢ ⟩. She has

       _____ ¢ left.

7. a. Eva has _____ ¢ .

    b. She buys a ⟨ 47 ¢ ⟩. She has

       _____ ¢ left.

8. a. Tommy has _____ ¢ .

    b. He buys a ⟨ 63 ¢ ⟩. He has

       _____ ¢ left.

9. a. Patrick has _____ ¢ .

    b. He buys a ⟨ 23 ¢ ⟩. He has

       _____ ¢ left.

10. a. Ted has _____ ¢ .

    b. He buys a ⟨ 85 ¢ ⟩. He has

       _____ ¢ left.

11. a. Sally has _____ ¢ .

    b. She buys a ⟨ 54 ¢ ⟩. She has

       _____ ¢ left.

See how much the customers pay for their food. Help the cashier check ✔ the fewest coins to show the change.

⑫ Kim buys a lollipop for 32¢ and pays . What is her change?

⑬ Joan buys a popsicle for 56¢ and pays . What is her change?

⑭ Eva buys a pretzel for 39¢ and pays . What is her change?

⑮ Jeffrey buys a cupcake for 86¢ and pays . What is his change?

⑯ Vivian buys an ice cream cone for 73¢ and pays . What is her change?

⑰ Bruce buys a bag of pop corn for 64¢ and pays . What is his change?

Mrs Ford works in a bakery. Help her solve the problems.

⑱ a. Mike buys 2 bread rolls for 16¢ each. How much does he need to pay?

_____ = _____

_____ ¢

  b. What is his change from 50¢ ?

_____ = _____

_____ ¢

⑲ a. Mr Jenn buys 2 cinnamon buns for 37¢ each. How much does he need to pay?

_____ = _____   _____ ¢

  b. What is his change from 80¢ ?

_____ = _____   _____ ¢

⑳ a. Mrs Winter buys 3 chocolate chip cookies for 18¢ each. How much does she need to pay?

_____ = _____   _____ ¢

  b. What is her change from $1?

_____ = _____   _____ ¢

㉑ a. Pam buys 3 brownies for 29¢ each. How much does she need to pay?

_____ = _____   _____ ¢

  b. What is her change from $1?

_____ = _____   _____ ¢

Colour $\frac{2}{3}$ of each shape.

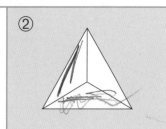
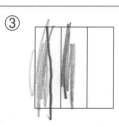
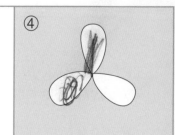

① ② ③ ④

Colour $\frac{1}{4}$ of each shape or group of shapes.

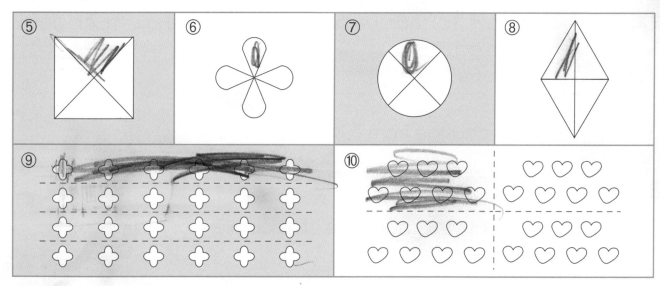

⑤ ⑥ ⑦ ⑧
⑨ ⑩

Write a fraction for the shaded part of each shape or group of shapes.

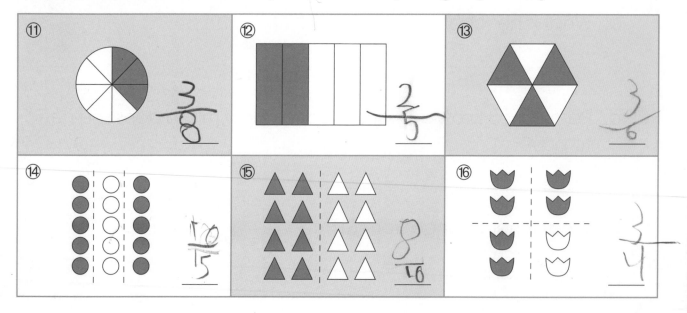

⑪ $\frac{3}{8}$

⑫ $\frac{2}{5}$

⑬ $\frac{3}{6}$

⑭ $\frac{10}{15}$

⑮ $\frac{8}{16}$

⑯ $\frac{3}{4}$

Colour the shapes to show each fraction. Write 'greater' or 'smaller' to complete each sentence.

⑰ a. $\frac{1}{3}$ b. $\frac{5}{6}$ c. $\frac{1}{2}$

d. $\frac{1}{3}$ is _____ than $\frac{5}{6}$; $\frac{5}{6}$ is _____ than $\frac{1}{2}$.

⑱ a. $\frac{2}{5}$ b. $\frac{3}{4}$ c. $\frac{1}{6}$

d. $\frac{2}{5}$ is _____ than $\frac{3}{4}$; $\frac{3}{4}$ is _____ than $\frac{1}{6}$.

Look at the children. Write the fractions.

⑲ How many children are there? _____ children

⑳ What fraction of the children are smiling? _____

㉑ What fraction of the children wear glasses? _____

㉒ What fraction of the children are boys? _____

㉓ What fraction of the children have curly hair? _____

㉔ What fraction of the children have long hair? _____

㉕ What fraction of the children with straight hair wear glasses? _____

Write a decimal number of the shaded part of each shape. Then answer the questions.

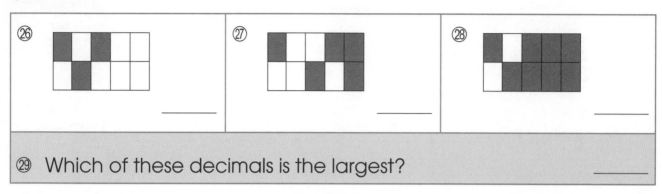

㉖ _____

㉗ _____

㉘ _____

㉙ Which of these decimals is the largest? _____

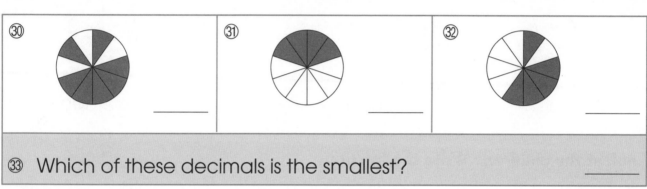

㉚ _____

㉛ _____

㉜ _____

㉝ Which of these decimals is the smallest? _____

Colour the shapes to show each decimal number.

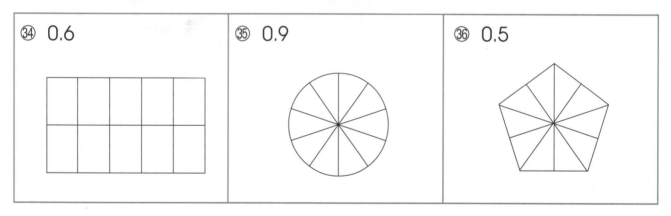

㉞ 0.6

㉟ 0.9

㊱ 0.5

Write a decimal number in words of the shaded part of each shape.

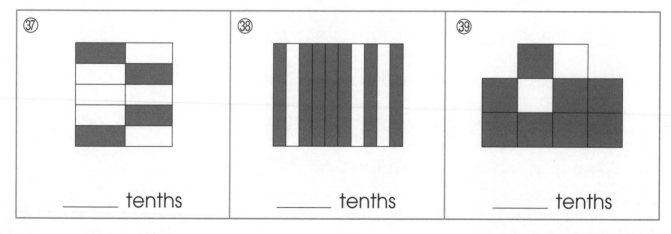

㊲ _____ tenths

㊳ _____ tenths

㊴ _____ tenths

Help the children write the amounts they have in decimals. Then fill in the blanks.

⑩ Kathy has 235¢ in her piggy bank.
She has $ ________ .

㊶ Paul has 261¢ in his piggy bank.
He has $ ________ .

㊷ Kathy has ________ more/less money than Paul.

㊸ 2.35 is ________ greater/smaller than 2.61.

㊹ Pat has 309¢ in her piggy bank. She has $ ________ .

㊺ Raymond has 325¢ in his piggy bank. He has $ ________ .

㊻ Pat has ________ more/less money than Raymond.

㊼ 3.09 is ________ greater/smaller than 3.25.

㊽ Susan has 75¢ in her piggy bank. She has $ ________ .

㊾ Katie has 250¢ in her piggy bank. She has $ ________ .

㊿ Jake has 175¢ in his piggy bank. He has $ ________ .

(51) Susan has ________ more/less money than Katie.

(52) Katie has ________ more/less money than Jake.

(53) 0.75 is ________ greater/smaller than 2.50.

(54) 2.50 is ________ greater/smaller than 1.75.

 **Graphs**

Five children each tossed a penny 10 times and recorded the number of heads they got. Use the graph to answer the questions.

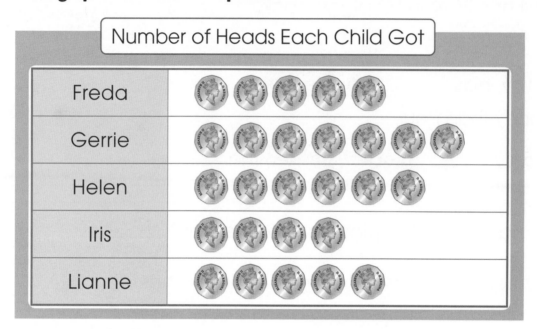

Number of Heads Each Child Got

① What is the title of the graph?

_____

② How many times did Iris get a head? _____ times

③ How many times did Helen get a head? _____ times

④ How many times did Gerrie get a tail? _____ times

⑤ How many times did Lianne get a tail? _____ times

⑥ Who got the most heads? _____

⑦ Who got the most tails? _____

⑧ How many times more did Gerrie get a head
  than Freda? _____ times more

⑨ How many times fewer did Gerrie get a tail
  than Iris? _____ times fewer

Use the graph to answer the questions.

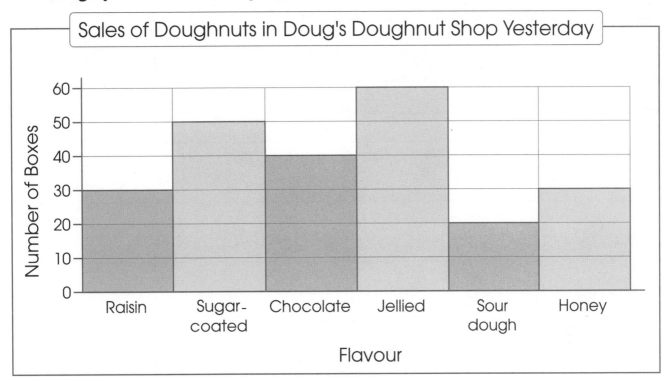

Sales of Doughnuts in Doug's Doughnut Shop Yesterday

⑩ What is the title of the graph?

_____

⑪ What type of graph is it?   _____

⑫ How many boxes of raisin doughnuts
     were sold?   _____ boxes

⑬ How many boxes of sugar-coated
     doughnuts were sold?   _____ boxes

⑭ Which was the most popular
     doughnut?   _____ doughnut

⑮ Which was the least popular
     doughnut?   _____ doughnut

⑯ Which kind of doughnut had the
     same sales as raisin doughnut?   _____ doughnut

⑰ If each box holds 6 doughnuts,
     how many chocolate doughnuts   _____ chocolate
     were sold in all?   doughnuts

Mrs Feler records the favourite summer activities in her class. Use her graph to complete the table and answer the questions.

Favourite Summer Activities in Mrs Feler's Class

Swimming

Soccer

Cycling

Hiking

⑱

Favourite Activity	Swimming	Soccer	Cycling	Hiking
Number of Children				

⑲ Which is the most popular summer activity? _____

⑳ Which is the least popular summer activity? _____

㉑ How many children are there in Mrs Feler's class? _____ children

Use the table above to complete the graph.

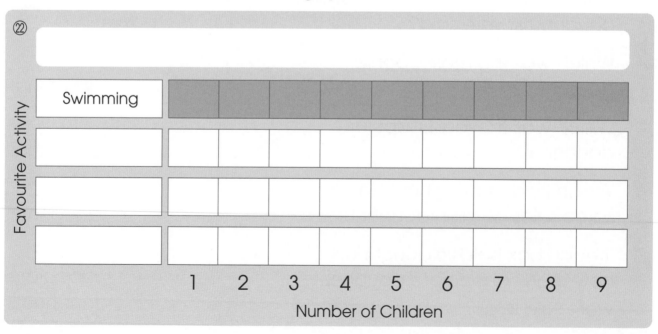

㉒

Swimming

Favourite Activity

1 2 3 4 5 6 7 8 9

Number of Children

The students of Riverview School were asked whether they had been to Florida. Use the chart below to complete the graph.

	Grade 1	Grade 2	Grade 3	Grade 4
Number of students	‖‖‖ ‖‖	‖‖‖ ‖‖‖ ‖‖	‖‖‖ ‖‖‖ ‖‖‖ ‖	‖‖‖ ‖‖‖ ‖‖‖‖

㉓

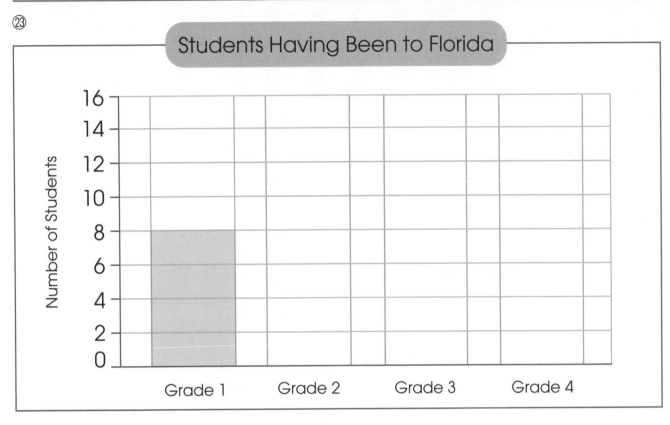

㉔ What is the title of the graph?

_____

㉕ Which grade has the most students who have been to Florida?   Grade _____

㉖ Which grade has 8 students who have been to Florida?   Grade _____

㉗ How many Grade 4 students have been to Florida?   _____ students

㉘ If 7 girls in Grade 2 have been to Florida, how many boys in Grade 2 have been to Florida?   _____ boys

㉙ How many students have been to Florida?   _____ students

10 Probability

Pam shuffles all her cards and lets Jimmy pick one. Answer the questions.

1	1	1	2	3	3	4	4	4	4
1	1	1	2	3	3	4	4	4	4
1	1	1	2	3	3	4	4	4	5

①   Are all the numbers equally likely to be picked?   _____

②   Which number is Jimmy most likely to pick?   _____

③   Which number is Jimmy most unlikely to pick?   _____

④   Is there a greater chance to pick a 1 or a 2 ?   _____

⑤   Is there a smaller chance to pick a 3 or a 4 ?   _____

⑥   Is there any chance to pick a 7 ?   _____

⑦   If the number card Jimmy picks is the same as the one he guesses, he will win the game. What number should Jimmy guess to have the greatest chance to win the game?   _____

⑧   What number does Jimmy guess if he has the smallest chance to win?   _____

⑨   If Pam takes away all the 4 , what number should Jimmy guess to have the greatest chance to win the game?   _____

Look at Jason's spinners and check ✔ the correct answers.

Spinner A 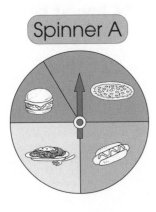 Spinner B  Spinner C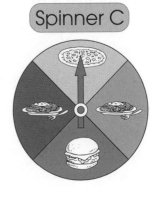

⑩ Which food is spinner A most likely to stop on?

Ⓐ 　　Ⓑ 　　Ⓒ 　　Ⓓ

⑪ Which food is spinner B most likely to stop on?

Ⓐ 　　Ⓑ 　　Ⓒ 　　Ⓓ

⑫ Which food is spinner C most likely to stop on?

Ⓐ 　　Ⓑ 　　Ⓒ 　　Ⓓ

⑬ Which is the best word to describe the chance of spinner A stopping

on ?

Ⓐ Likely　　　Ⓑ Unlikely　　　Ⓒ Probably　　　Ⓓ Never

⑭ Which is the best word to describe the chance of spinner B stopping

on ?

Ⓐ Likely　　　Ⓑ Unlikely　　　Ⓒ Probably　　　Ⓓ Never

⑮ Which is the best word to describe the chance of spinner C stopping

on ?

Ⓐ Likely　　　Ⓑ Unlikely　　　Ⓒ Probably　　　Ⓓ Never

⑯ Which spinner should Jason spin if he wants to get  ?

Ⓐ Spinner A　　Ⓑ Spinner B　　Ⓒ Spinner C

Write the price of each snack. Then calculate and check ✔ the fewest coins to show the change for each child.

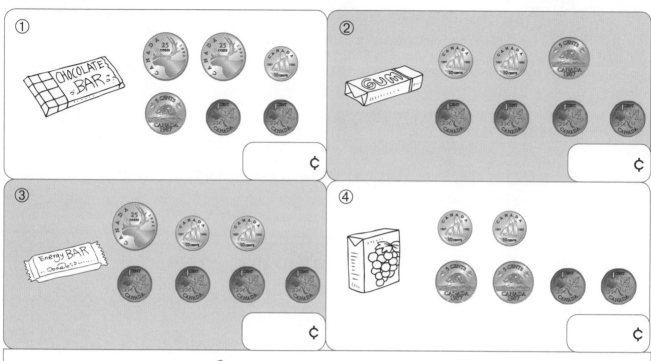

① CHOCOLATE BAR _____ ¢

② GUM _____ ¢

③ Energy BAR _____ ¢

④ _____ ¢

⑤ Harry buys a CHOCOLATE BAR. What is his change from $1?

a. _____ = _____   _____ ¢ change

b.

⑥ Freda buys 1 Energy BAR and 1 🍇. What is her change from $1?

a. _____ = _____   _____ ¢ change

b.

⑦ Betty buys 2 GUM. What is her change from $1?

a. _____ = _____   _____ ¢ change

b.

Draw the clock hands to show the times and calculate the perimeter of each digital clock.

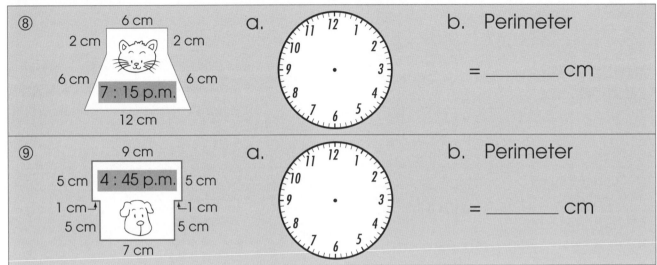

⑧

6 cm
2 cm · 2 cm
6 cm · 6 cm
7 : 15 p.m.
12 cm

a.

b. Perimeter

= _____ cm

⑨

9 cm
5 cm · 4 : 45 p.m. · 5 cm
1 cm · 1 cm
5 cm · 5 cm
7 cm

a.

b. Perimeter

= _____ cm

Measure and write the lengths of the bracelets. Then answer the questions.

⑩ (A) ∘○○○○○○○○○○○○○○○○○○○○○

(B) ∘○○○○○○○○○○○○○○○

(A) : _____ cm   (B) : _____ cm

⑪ Which bracelet is shorter?   Bracelet _____

⑫ Which bracelet is a better unit for measuring
the width of a door?   Bracelet _____

⑬ Bracelet C is 5 cm longer than bracelet A.
How long is bracelet C?   _____ cm

See how heavy each jar of beads is. Then write the numbers.

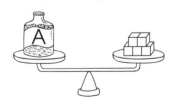
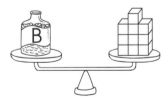

⑭ Jar A has the same weight as _____ ⬜ .

⑮ Jar B has the same weight as _____ ⬜ .

⑯ Jar B has the same weight as _____ jar A.

Look at the graph. Then answer the questions.

Time for Homework Yesterday

less than half an hour | half an hour | one hour | one and a half hours | two hours

Time Spent

⑰ What is the title of the graph?

_____

⑱ What type of graph is it? _____

⑲ How many students spent half an hour on
homework? _____ students

⑳ How many students spent one hour or more
on homework? _____ students

㉑ 4 boys spent one hour on homework. How
many girls spent one hour on homework? _____ girls

Complete the bar graph to show the information on the above graph.

㉒

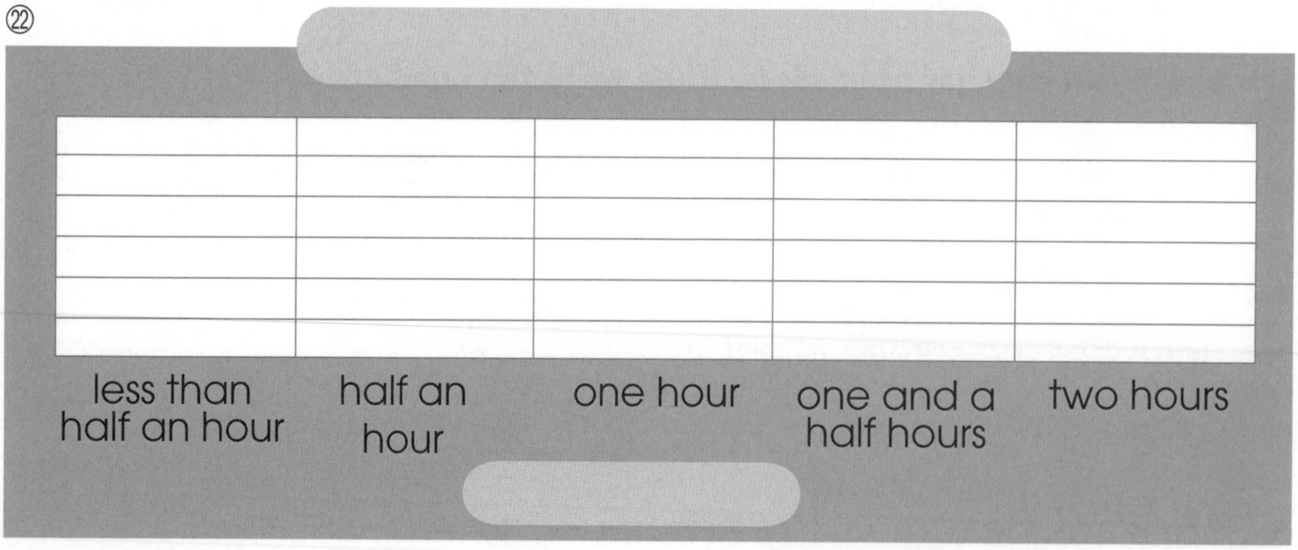

less than half an hour | half an hour | one hour | one and a half hours | two hours

Write a fraction and a decimal for the shaded part of each shape.

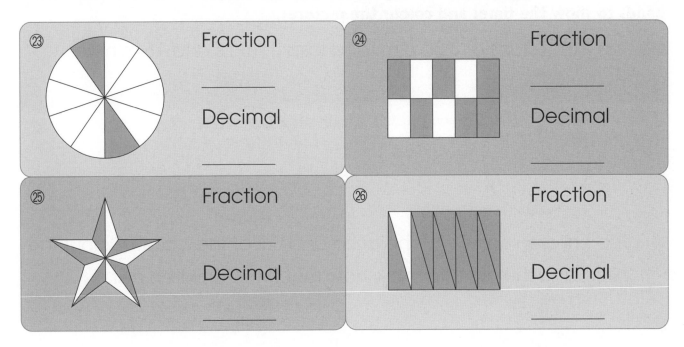

㉓ Fraction

_____

Decimal

_____

㉔ Fraction

_____

Decimal

_____

㉕ Fraction

_____

Decimal

_____

㉖ Fraction

_____

Decimal

_____

Peter picks one marble from the bag. Help him answer the questions.

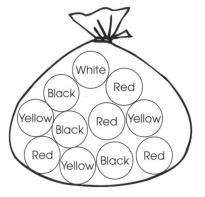

㉗ Are all the marbles equally likely to be picked?   _____

㉘ What colour is Peter most likely to pick?   _____

㉙ What colour is Peter most unlikely to pick?   _____

㉚ Is there any chance to pick a ⟮Yellow⟯ ?   _____

㉛ Is there any chance to pick a ⟮Blue⟯ ?   _____

㉜ Is there a greater chance to pick a ⟮Black⟯ or a ⟮Red⟯ ?   _____

㉝ How many marbles are there in the bag?   _____ marbles

㉞ What fraction of the marbles are red?   _____

㉟ What fraction of the marbles are yellow?   _____

Danielle invites some friends to her birthday party. Help Danielle draw the clock hands to show the times and colour the pictures.

㊱ The party starts at 3:30 p.m. and lasts 2 hours and 15 minutes.

a.
Start

b.
End

㊲ The children eat $\frac{5}{8}$ of the pizza and 0.7 of the cake. Colour the pizza and the cake to show how much the children eat.

Pizza

a.

Cake

b.

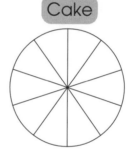

Use the graph to answer the questions.

Party Toys

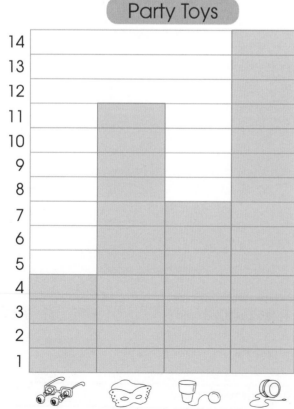

㊳ There are _____ ,

_____ _____ , _____ _____

and _____ _____ .

㊴ There are _____ more

than _____ .

㊵ There are _____ party toys in all.

㊶ Each _____ costs 23¢ .

4 _____ cost _____ ¢.

Section II

Overview

The previous section included a wide variety of skills in the numeration, measurement, geometry and data management strands.

This section, however, places the emphasis entirely on multiplication and division skills including division with remainders. Concrete materials and pictures are used to show multiplication as repeated addition and division as the opposite of multiplication.

Introducing Multiplication

How many cakes are there on 4 plates?

    2 + 2 + 2 + 2 = 8   There are 8 cakes.

How many groups are there?   <u>4 groups.</u>

How many cakes are there in each group? <u>2 cakes.</u>

How many cakes are there?   <u>8 cakes.</u>

   4 groups of 2 = 4 twos = 4 times 2 = 4 x 2 = 8

HINTS:

- Multiplication is a short way to add groups of the same size.

- " X " means MULTIPLY.

- There are different ways to represent multiplication.

  e.g.   3 groups of 2 = 3 twos
       = 3 times 2 = 6

     or use a multiplication sentence

    3 x 2 = 6
    ↑   ↑   ↑
  factor factor product

Count and write the numbers.

①

  2 → 4 → 6 → _____

  4 twos are _____ .

  There are _____ .

②

  3 → 6 → 9 → _____ → _____

  5 threes are _____ .

  There are _____ 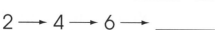 .

③

  5 → 10 → _____ → _____ → _____ → _____ → _____

  7 fives are _____ .

  There are _____  .

④

  4 → 8 → _____ → _____ → _____ → _____

  6 fours are _____ .

  There are _____ .

Add and complete.

⑤

2 + _____ + _____ + _____ + _____

= _____ times 2

= _____

⑥

4 + _____ + _____

= _____ times 4

= _____

⑦

5 + _____ + _____

= _____ times 5

= _____

⑧

6 + _____

= _____ times 6

= _____

Circle the correct number of shapes in each diagram. Complete the statements.

⑨ Circle in groups of 4.

_____ fours are _____ .

_____ times 4 = _____

⑩ Circle in groups of 6.

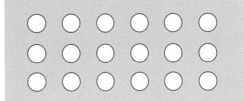

_____ sixes are _____ .

_____ times 6 = _____

⑪ Circle in groups of 7.

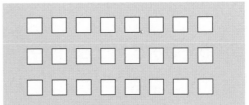

_____ sevens are _____ .

_____ times 7 = _____

⑫ Circle in groups of 3.

_____ threes are _____ .

_____ times 3 = _____

Complete the addition and multiplication sentences for each diagram.

⑬

2 + ____ + ____ + ____ + ____ + ____ = ____ x 2 = ____

⑭

3 + ____ + ____ + ____ + ____ = ____ x 3 = ____

⑮

4 + ____ + ____ + ____ + ____ = ____ x 4 = ____

⑯

5 + ____ + ____ = ____ x 5 = ____

· ·

Complete.

⑰   9 + 9 + 9 + 9 + 9 = ____ nines = ____ times 9

= ____ x 9 = ____

⑱   8 + 8 + 8 + 8 + 8 + 8 + 8 = ____ eights = ____ times 8

= ____ x 8 = ____

⑲   5 + 5 + 5 + 5 = ____ fives = ____ times 5

= ____ x 5 = ____

⑳   3 + 3 + 3 + 3 + 3 + 3 = ____ threes = ____ times 3

= ____ x 3 = ____

Match. Write the letters in the ◯.

A.	8 times 2	**B.**	3 sevens	**C.**	4 times 3
D.	6 fives	**E.**	4 times 6	**F.**	2 nines
G.	3 times 8	**H.**	5 times 7	**I.**	5 fives

㉑ 3 x 7 ◯   ㉒ 2 x 9 ◯   ㉓ 6 x 5 ◯

㉔ 5 x 5 ◯   ㉕ 8 x 2 ◯   ㉖ 3 x 8 ◯

㉗ 4 x 6 ◯   ㉘ 5 x 7 ◯   ㉙ 4 x 3 ◯

Answer the questions.

㉚

How many groups are there?   _____ groups.

How many in each group?   _____ .

How many are there?

_____ groups of _____ = _____ x _____ = _____

There are _____ .

Move one stick in each problem to make the number sentences true.

① | + || + ||| = ||||

② |||||| — || — | = |

2 Multiplying by 2 or 5

1.

   4 twos = 4 x 2 = 8

   $$\begin{array}{r} 2 \\ \times \quad 4 \\ \hline 8 \end{array}$$

2.

   3 fives = 5 x 3 = 15

   $$\begin{array}{r} 5 \\ \times \quad 3 \\ \hline 1\;5 \end{array}$$

HINTS:

- Multiplication facts can be written in two different ways.

  e.g. 2 x 5 = 10 $\begin{array}{r} 5 \\ \times \quad 2 \\ \hline 10 \end{array}$

  product

- Count by 2's or 5's to find the products when multiplying by 2 or 5.

- The product of any number multiplied by 2 is an even number.

- The product of any number multiplied by 5 has 0 or 5 at the ones place.

Count the birds' legs. Complete the multiplication sentences and the table.

① ___1___ times 2

  = ___1___ x 2 = ___2___

②

  _____ times 2 = _____ x 2 = _____

③

  _____ times 2 = _____ x 2 = _____

④ 4 times 2
  = _____ x 2
  = _____

⑤ 5 times 2
  = _____ x 2
  = _____

⑥ 6 times 2
  = _____ x 2
  = _____

⑦ 7 times 2
  = _____ x 2
  = _____

⑧ 8 times 2
  = _____ x 2
  = _____

⑨ 9 times 2
  = _____ x 2
  = _____

⑩

x	1	2	3	4	5	6	7	8	9
2									

Count the number of flowers. Complete the multiplication sentences and the table below.

⑪  ___1___ times 5 = ___1___ x 5 = ___5___

⑫  _____ times 5 = _____ x 5 = _____

⑬ _____ times 5 = _____ x 5 = _____

⑭ _____ times 5 = _____ x 5 = _____

⑮ _____ times 5 = _____ x 5 = _____

⑯ _____ times 5 = _____ x 5 = _____

⑰ _____ times 5 = _____ x 5 = _____

⑱ _____ times 5 = _____ x 5 = _____

⑲  _____ times 5 = _____ x 5 = _____

⑳

x	1	2	3	4	5	6	7	8	9
5									

Do the multiplication.

㉑ $8 \times 2 =$ _____   ㉒ $4 \times 5 =$ _____   ㉓ $7 \times 5 =$ _____

㉔ $5 \times 2 =$ _____   ㉕ $3 \times 5 =$ _____   ㉖ $6 \times 2 =$ _____

㉗ $5 \times 5 =$ _____   ㉘ $2 \times 2 =$ _____   ㉙ $4 \times 2 =$ _____

㉚ $8 \times 5 =$ _____   ㉛ $3 \times 2 =$ _____   ㉜ $2 \times 5 =$ _____

㉝ $1 \times 2 =$ _____   ㉞ $9 \times 5 =$ _____   ㉟ $6 \times 5 =$ _____

㊱ $9 \times 2 =$ _____   ㊲ $1 \times 5 =$ _____   ㊳ $7 \times 2 =$ _____

㊴ $2 \times 5 =$ _____   ㊵ $5 \times 2 =$ _____   ㊶ $3 \times 2 =$ _____

㊷ $9 \times 2 =$ _____   ㊸ $8 \times 2 =$ _____   ㊹ $5 \times 5 =$ _____

㊺
$$\begin{array}{r} 5 \\ \times\ 3 \\ \hline \end{array}$$

㊻
$$\begin{array}{r} 5 \\ \times\ 8 \\ \hline \end{array}$$

㊼
$$\begin{array}{r} 2 \\ \times\ 4 \\ \hline \end{array}$$

㊽
$$\begin{array}{r} 2 \\ \times\ 6 \\ \hline \end{array}$$

㊾
$$\begin{array}{r} 2 \\ \times\ 2 \\ \hline \end{array}$$

㊿
$$\begin{array}{r} 2 \\ \times\ 7 \\ \hline \end{array}$$

51
$$\begin{array}{r} 5 \\ \times\ 7 \\ \hline \end{array}$$

52
$$\begin{array}{r} 5 \\ \times\ 4 \\ \hline \end{array}$$

53
$$\begin{array}{r} 5 \\ \times\ 1 \\ \hline \end{array}$$

54
$$\begin{array}{r} 2 \\ \times\ 9 \\ \hline \end{array}$$

55
$$\begin{array}{r} 5 \\ \times\ 6 \\ \hline \end{array}$$

56
$$\begin{array}{r} 2 \\ \times\ 1 \\ \hline \end{array}$$

Solve the problems. Show your work.

(57) There are 5 toes on one foot.

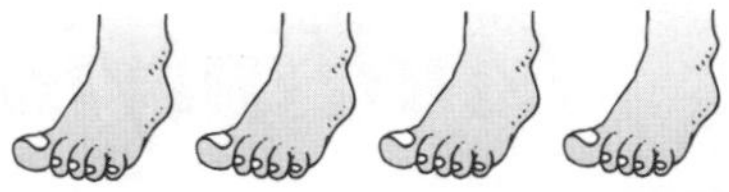

How many toes are there on 4 feet?

____ x ____ = ____

There are ____ toes on 4 feet.

$$\begin{array}{r} 5 \\ \times\ 4 \\ \hline \end{array}$$

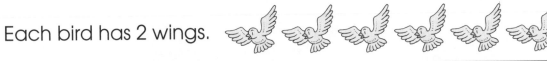

(58) Each bird has 2 wings.

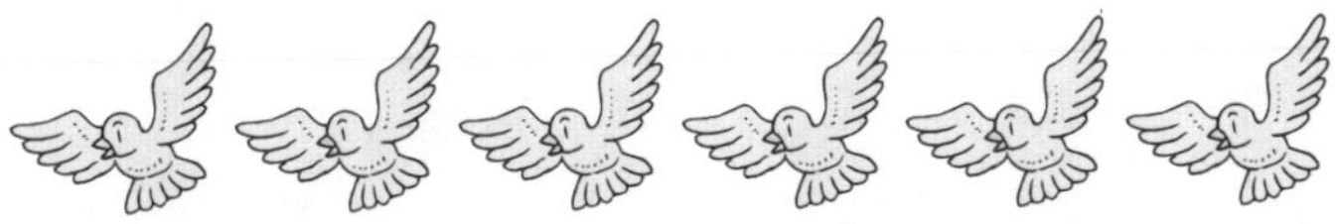

How many wings do 6 birds have?

____ x ____ = ____

6 birds have ____ wings.

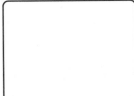

(59) Each frog has 2 eyes.

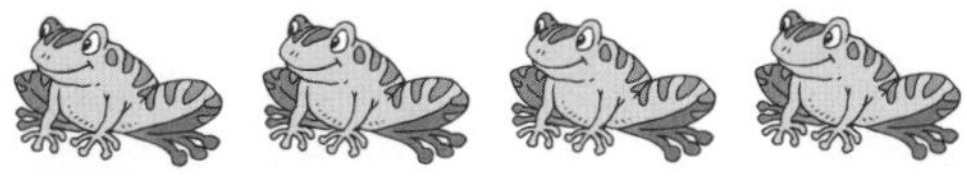

How many eyes do 4 frogs have?

____ x ____ = ____

4 frogs have ____ eyes.

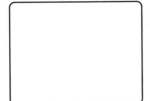

(60) There are 5 bananas in each bunch.

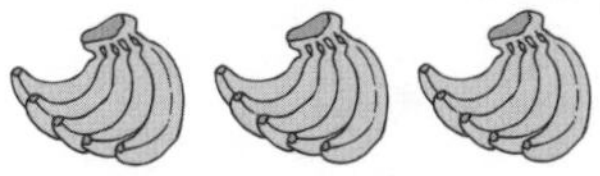

How many bananas are there in 3 bunches?

____ x ____ = ____

There are ____ bananas in 3 bunches.

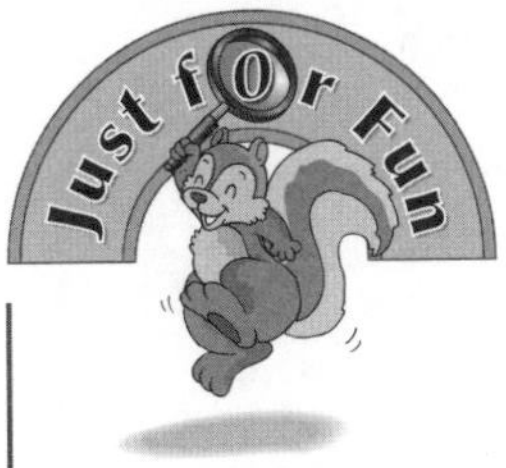

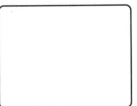

Put 1 to 9 into the boxes so that the sum of the numbers in each group is 11.

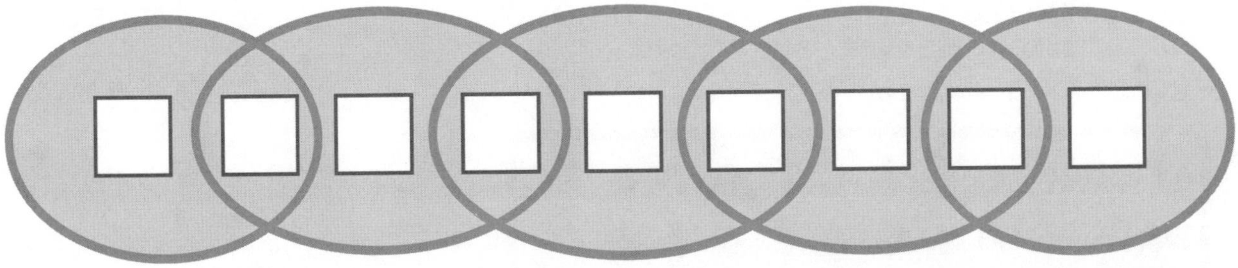

3 Multiplying by 3 or 4

1.

    5 threes = 5 x 3 = 15

    $$\begin{array}{r} 3 \\ \times\ \ 5 \\ \hline 1\ 5 \end{array}$$

2.

    6 fours = 6 x 4 = 24

    $$\begin{array}{r} 4 \\ \times\ \ 6 \\ \hline 2\ 4 \end{array}$$

Circle the shapes in groups of 3. Then complete the multiplication sentences and the table.

> HINTS:
>
> - Count by 3's or 4's to find the products when multiplying by 3 or 4.
> - The product of any number multiplied by 4 is an even number.
> - The product of any even number multipled by 3 is an even number.
> - The product of any odd number multiplied by 3 is an odd number.

①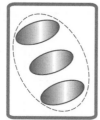

   __1__ times 3
   = __1__ x 3 = __3__

②

   ____ times 3
   = ____ x 3 = ____

③

   ____ times 3
   = ____ x 3 = ____

④

   ____ times 3
   = ____ x 3 = ____

⑤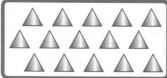

   ____ times 3
   = ____ x 3 = ____

⑥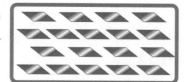

   ____ times 3
   = ____ x 3 = ____

⑦

   ____ times 3
   = ____ x 3 = ____

⑧

   _____ times 3
   = _____ x 3 = _____

⑨

x	1	2	3	4	5	6	7	8	9
3									

Count the number of wings on the dragonflies. Then complete the multiplication sentences.

⑩   1 dragonfly has 4 wings.   1 x 4 = _____

⑪   2 dragonflies have _____ wings.   2 x 4 = _____

⑫   3 dragonflies have _____ wings.   _____ x 4 = _____

⑬   4 dragonflies have _____ wings.   _____ x 4 = _____

⑭   5 dragonflies have _____ wings.   _____ x 4 = _____

⑮   6 dragonflies have _____ wings.   _____ x 4 = _____

⑯   7 dragonflies have _____ wings.   _____ x 4 = _____

⑰   8 dragonflies have _____ wings.   _____ x 4 = _____

⑱   9 dragonflies have _____ wings.   _____ x 4 = _____

Little Frog jumps 4 spaces every time. Complete its path and list the numbers it lands on.

⑲

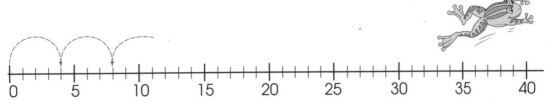

4
_____ , _____ , _____ , _____ , _____ , _____ , _____ , _____ ,

Do the multiplication.

⑳ 5 x 3 = ______ ㉑ 7 x 4 = ______ ㉒ 4 x 4 = ______

㉓ 3 x 3 = ______ ㉔ 2 x 3 = ______ ㉕ 3 x 4 = ______

㉖ 6 x 4 = ______ ㉗ 8 x 4 = ______ ㉘ 7 x 3 = ______

㉙ 1 x 4 = ______ ㉚ 4 x 3 = ______ ㉛ 6 x 3 = ______

㉜ 8 x 3 = ______ ㉝ 9 x 4 = ______ ㉞ 5 x 4 = ______

㉟ 9 x 3 = ______ ㊱ 1 x 3 = ______ ㊲ 2 x 4 = ______

㊳ 5 x 4 = ______ ㊴ 6 x 4 = ______ ㊵ 9 x 3 = ______

㊶ 7 x 3 = ______ ㊷ 3 x 3 = ______ ㊸ 8 x 4 = ______

㊹ $\begin{array}{r} 3 \\ \times \quad 8 \\ \hline \end{array}$

㊺ $\begin{array}{r} 4 \\ \times \quad 9 \\ \hline \end{array}$

㊻ $\begin{array}{r} 3 \\ \times \quad 6 \\ \hline \end{array}$

㊼ $\begin{array}{r} 4 \\ \times \quad 7 \\ \hline \end{array}$

㊽ $\begin{array}{r} 4 \\ \times \quad 4 \\ \hline \end{array}$

㊾ $\begin{array}{r} 3 \\ \times \quad 5 \\ \hline \end{array}$

㊿ $\begin{array}{r} 4 \\ \times \quad 3 \\ \hline \end{array}$

(51) $\begin{array}{r} 3 \\ \times \quad 1 \\ \hline \end{array}$

(52) $\begin{array}{r} 3 \\ \times \quad 2 \\ \hline \end{array}$

(53) $\begin{array}{r} 4 \\ \times \quad 1 \\ \hline \end{array}$

(54) $\begin{array}{r} 3 \\ \times \quad 4 \\ \hline \end{array}$

(55) $\begin{array}{r} 4 \\ \times \quad 2 \\ \hline \end{array}$

Solve the problems. Show your work.

56 There are 4 tires on one car.
How many tires are there on 5 cars?

_____ x _____ = _____

There are _____ tires.

$\begin{array}{r} 4 \\ \times\ 5 \\ \hline \end{array}$

---

57 There are 3 cups on each tray.
How many cups are there on 4 trays?

_____ x _____ = _____

There are _____ cups.

$\begin{array}{r} \\ \times\ \\ \hline \end{array}$

---

58 Each dog has 4 legs.
How many legs do 7 dogs have?

_____ x _____ = _____

7 dogs have _____ legs.

$\begin{array}{r} \\ \times\ \\ \hline \end{array}$

---

59 Each pencil box costs $3.
How much do 8 pencil boxes cost?

_____ x _____ = _____

8 pencil boxes cost $ _____ .

$\begin{array}{r} \\ \times\ \\ \hline \end{array}$

Just for Fun

Match. Find the dogs' kennels.

 3 X 4    5 X 3    8 X 2    6 X 3

 16   12    18   15

Multiplying by 6 or 7

1.    4 groups of 6
= 4 x 6 = 24

2.    5 groups of 7
= 5 x 7 = 35

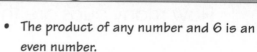

HINTS:

- The product of any number and 6 is an even number.

- The product of 7 and any even number is an even number. The product of 7 and any odd number is an odd number.

   e.g.   4 x 7 = 28 ⟵ even number
         3 x 7 = 21 ⟵ odd number

Count the number of cubes. Then complete the multiplication sentences and the table.

①

_____1_____ times 6

= ____1____ x 6 = ____6____

②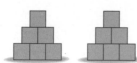

_____ times 6

= _____ x 6 = _____

③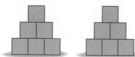

_____ times 6

= _____ x 6 = _____

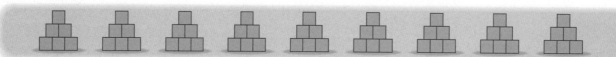

④ 4 sixes

= _____ x 6

= _____

⑤ 5 sixes

= _____ x 6

= _____

⑥ 6 sixes

= _____ x 6

= _____

⑦ 7 sixes

= _____ x 6

= _____

⑧ 8 sixes

= _____ x 6

= _____

⑨ 9 sixes

= _____ x 6

= _____

⑩

X	1	2	3	4	5	6	7	8	9
6									

Count the number of stars on the cards. Then complete the multiplication sentences.

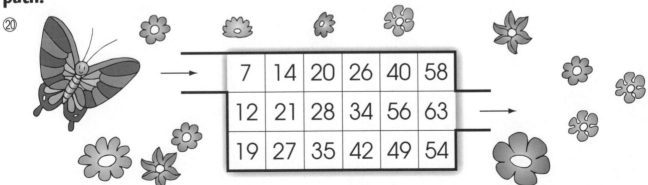

⑪ 1 card has 7 stars. 1 x 7 = _____

⑫ 2 cards have _____ stars. 2 x 7 = _____

⑬ 3 cards have _____ stars. _____ x 7 = _____

⑭ 4 cards have _____ stars. _____ x 7 = _____

⑮ 5 cards have _____ stars. _____ x 7 = _____

⑯ 6 cards have _____ stars. _____ x 7 = _____

⑰ 7 cards have _____ stars. _____ x 7 = _____

⑱ 8 cards have _____ stars. _____ x 7 = _____

⑲ 9 cards have _____ stars. _____ x 7 = _____

Count by 7's. Help Little Butterfly find its path through the flowers. Colour its path.

⑳

7	14	20	26	40	58
12	21	28	34	56	63
19	27	35	42	49	54

Do the Multiplication.

㉑ $4 \times 6 =$ _____   ㉒ $5 \times 7 =$ _____   ㉓ $3 \times 7 =$ _____

㉔ $3 \times 6 =$ _____   ㉕ $6 \times 6 =$ _____   ㉖ $8 \times 7 =$ _____

㉗ $2 \times 7 =$ _____   ㉘ $8 \times 6 =$ _____   ㉙ $9 \times 6 =$ _____

㉚ $4 \times 7 =$ _____   ㉛ $1 \times 7 =$ _____   ㉜ $5 \times 6 =$ _____

㉝ $2 \times 6 =$ _____   ㉞ $6 \times 7 =$ _____   ㉟ $7 \times 7 =$ _____

㊱ $7 \times 6 =$ _____   ㊲ $9 \times 7 =$ _____   ㊳ $1 \times 6 =$ _____

㊴ $3 \times 7 =$ _____   ㊵ $5 \times 6 =$ _____   ㊶ $3 \times 6 =$ _____

㊷ $9 \times 6 =$ _____   ㊸ $2 \times 7 =$ _____   ㊹ $5 \times 7 =$ _____

㊺ $5 \times 3 =$ _____   ㊻ $4 \times 5 =$ _____   ㊼ $3 \times 2 =$ _____

㊽ $\begin{array}{r} 7 \\ \times\ 1 \\ \hline \end{array}$	㊾ $\begin{array}{r} 6 \\ \times\ 4 \\ \hline \end{array}$	㊿ $\begin{array}{r} 7 \\ \times\ 9 \\ \hline \end{array}$	�51 $\begin{array}{r} 6 \\ \times\ 6 \\ \hline \end{array}$
�52 $\begin{array}{r} 6 \\ \times\ 8 \\ \hline \end{array}$	�53 $\begin{array}{r} 7 \\ \times\ 7 \\ \hline \end{array}$	�54 $\begin{array}{r} 6 \\ \times\ 1 \\ \hline \end{array}$	�55 $\begin{array}{r} 7 \\ \times\ 8 \\ \hline \end{array}$
�56 $\begin{array}{r} 7 \\ \times\ 6 \\ \hline \end{array}$	�57 $\begin{array}{r} 6 \\ \times\ 2 \\ \hline \end{array}$	�58 $\begin{array}{r} 7 \\ \times\ 4 \\ \hline \end{array}$	�59 $\begin{array}{r} 6 \\ \times\ 7 \\ \hline \end{array}$

Solve the problems. Show your work.

⑥⓪ A little bee has 6 legs.
How many legs do 8 bees have?

_____ = _____

8 bees have _____ legs.

⑥① There are 7 buttons on a shirt.
How many buttons are there on 5 shirts?

_____ = _____

There are _____ buttons on 5 shirts.

⑥② There are 6 shelves in a cupboard.
How many shelves are there in 4 cupboards?

_____ = _____

There are _____ shelves in 4 cupboards.

⑥③ There are 7 cakes on a plate.
How many cakes are there on 6 plates?

_____ = _____

There are _____ cakes.

Write + or – in the ◯ to make the number sentences true.

① 3 ◯ 2 ◯ 1 = 0
② 3 ◯ 2 ◯ 1 = 2
③ 3 ◯ 2 ◯ 1 = 4
④ 3 ◯ 2 ◯ 1 = 6

5 Multiplication Facts to 49

1. 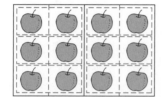 =

   3 twos = 2 threes
   3 x 2 = 2 x 3 = 6

2. 2 times 6 = 2 x 6 = 12

   4 times 3 = 4 x 3 = 12

   6 times 2 = 6 x 2 = 12

HINTS:

- When you change the order of multiplication, the product remains the same.

  e.g.   2 x 3 = 3 x 2 = 6

- A number may be obtained by adding groups of the same size.

  e.g. 12 = 6 + 6
  = 2 x 6   2 groups of 6
  12 = 3 + 3 + 3 + 3
  = 4 x 3   4 groups of 3
  12 = 2 + 2 + 2 + 2 + 2 + 2
  = 6 x 2   6 groups of 2

Circle the animals in groups of different sizes. Then complete the multiplication sentences.

① a. Circle in groups of 2.

   _____ x 2 = _____

   b. Circle in groups of 4.

   _____ x 4 = _____

   c.   _____ x 2 = _____ x 4

   = _____

② a. Circle in groups of 3.

   _____ x 3 = _____

   b. Circle in groups of 5.

   _____ x 5 = _____

   c. _____ x 3 = _____ x 5 = _____

③ a. Circle in groups of 4.

   _____ x 4 = _____

   b. Circle in groups of 3.

   _____ x 3 = _____

   c. _____ x 4 = _____ x 3 = _____

Complete the following multiplication sentences.

④ 2 x 5 = _____

5 x 2 = _____

2 x 5 = _____ x 2

⑥ 4 x 7 = _____

7 x 4 = _____

_____ x 7 = 7 x 4

⑧ 5 x 6 = _____

6 x 5 = _____

5 x _____ = 6 x _____

⑩ 3 x _____ = 7 x 3

= _____

⑫ 2 x 6 = _____ x 2

= _____

⑭ 4 x _____ = 6 x 4

= _____

⑤ 6 x 3 = _____

3 x 6 = _____

6 x 3 = 3 x _____

⑦ 2 x 7 = _____

7 x 2 = _____

2 x _____ = 7 x 2

⑨ 4 x 5 = _____

5 x 4 = _____

_____ x 5 = _____ x 4

⑪ _____ x 6 = 6 x 4

= _____

⑬ 5 x 7 = 7 x _____

= _____

⑮ 2 x _____ = 9 x 2

= _____

Write True (T) or False (F) in the ( ).

⑯ 5 + 2 = 2 x 5 ( )

⑱ 3 x 7 = 7 x 3 ( )

⑳ 6 + 7 = 7 + 6 ( )

㉒ 6 + 6 = 6 x 2 ( )

⑰ 2 + 2 = 2 x 2 ( )

⑲ 2 + 6 = 6 + 2 ( )

㉑ 5 + 5 = 2 + 5 ( )

㉓ 3 x 4 = 4 x 3 ( )

Circle the insects in groups of different sizes and complete the multiplication sentences.

㉔　a. Circle in groups of 2.

_____ groups of 2

= _____ x 2

= _____

b. Circle in groups of 3.

_____ groups of 3

= _____ x 3

= _____

c. Circle in groups of 6.

_____ groups of 6

= _____ x 6

= _____

d. _____ x 2 = _____ x 3 = _____ x 6 = _____

㉕　a. Circle in groups of 3.

_____ groups of 3

= _____ x 3

= _____

b. Circle in groups of 4.

_____ groups of 4

= _____ x 4

= _____

c. Circle in groups of 6.

_____ groups of 6

= _____ x 6

= _____

d. _____ x 3 = _____ x 4 = _____ x 6 = _____

Answer the questions. Fill in the missing numbers.

㉖  A bag of sweets is shared equally among 7 children. Each child has 6 sweets.

If it is shared equally among 6 children, each child can have _____ sweets.

㉗  A bag of cookies is shared equally among 6 children. Each child has 5 cookies.

If it is shared equally among 5 children, each child can have _____ cookies.

㉘  A box of lollipops is shared equally among 5 girls. Each girl has 4 lollipops.

If it is shared equally among 4 girls, each girl has _____ lollipops.

㉙ 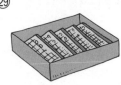 Sally puts her chocolate bars equally into 3 boxes. Each box has 5 chocolate bars.

If she puts the chocolate bars equally into 5 boxes, each box will have _____ chocolate bars.

㉚  Tom has enough money to buy 6 chocolate bars at $3 each.

He can buy _____ chocolate bars if the price of each chocolate bar is reduced to $2.

 **Just for Fun**

Match the cakes with the boxes.

 4 x 6   3 x 7   4 x 5   6 x 3

 7 x 3   8 x 3   9 x 2   5 x 4

6 Multiplying by 8, 9, 0 or 1

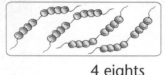

EXAMPLES

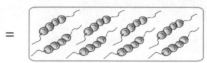

4 eights = 8 fours
4 x 8 = 8 x 4 = 32

1. How many cakes are there?

```
   1
x  9
___
   9
```

1 + 1 + 1 + 1 + 1 + 1 + 1 + 1 + 1 = 9 x 1 = 9
There are 9 cakes.

2. How many cakes are there?

```
   0
x  6
___
   0
```

0 + 0 + 0 + 0 + 0 + 0 = 6 x 0 = 0
There are 0 cakes.

HINTS:

- Practise the 8 times and 9 times tables by recalling the multiplication tables of 2 to 7.

- The product of 8 and any number is always an even number.

- Multiply any number by 1, the number will stay the same.

- Multiply any number by 0, the product will be 0.

Look at the pictures and complete the multiplication sentences.

①

_____ times 1 = _____ x 1 = _____

There are _____ fish.

②

_____ times 0 = _____ x 0 = _____   There are _____ fish.

③

_____ times 8 = _____ x 8 = _____   There are _____ marbles.

④

_____ times 8 = _____ x 8 = _____   There are _____ crayons.

68   COMPLETE MATHSMART (GRADE 3)

Complete the multiplication sentences and multiplication table.

⑤   1 times eight = 1 x 8 = 8 x _____ = _____

⑥   2 times eight = 2 x 8 = 8 x _____ = _____

⑦   3 times eight = 3 x 8 = 8 x _____ = _____

⑧   4 times eight = 4 x 8 = 8 x _____ = _____

⑨   5 times eight = 5 x 8 = 8 x _____ = _____

⑩   6 times eight = 6 x 8 = 8 x _____ = _____

⑪   7 times eight = 7 x 8 = 8 x _____ = _____

⑫

x	1	2	3	4	5	6	7	8	9
8									

⑬   1 x 9 = 9 x _____

       = _____

⑭   2 x 9 = 9 x _____

       = _____

⑮   3 x 9 = 9 x _____

       = _____

⑯   4 x 9 = 9 x _____

       = _____

⑰   5 x 9 = 9 x _____

       = _____

⑱   6 x 9 = 9 x _____

       = _____

⑲   7 x 9 = 9 x _____

       = _____

⑳   8 x 9 = 9 x _____

       = _____

㉑   9 + 9 + 9 + 9 + 9 + 9 + 9 + 9 + 9

   = 9 x 9 = _____

Do the multiplication.

㉒
$$\begin{array}{r} 1 \\ \times\ 4 \\ \hline \end{array}$$

㉓
$$\begin{array}{r} 0 \\ \times\ 5 \\ \hline \end{array}$$

㉔
$$\begin{array}{r} 0 \\ \times\ 8 \\ \hline \end{array}$$

㉕
$$\begin{array}{r} 1 \\ \times\ 3 \\ \hline \end{array}$$

㉖
$$\begin{array}{r} 8 \\ \times\ 3 \\ \hline \end{array}$$

㉗
$$\begin{array}{r} 9 \\ \times\ 4 \\ \hline \end{array}$$

㉘
$$\begin{array}{r} 8 \\ \times\ 8 \\ \hline \end{array}$$

㉙
$$\begin{array}{r} 9 \\ \times\ 2 \\ \hline \end{array}$$

㉚
$$\begin{array}{r} 9 \\ \times\ 9 \\ \hline \end{array}$$

㉛
$$\begin{array}{r} 8 \\ \times\ 2 \\ \hline \end{array}$$

㉜
$$\begin{array}{r} 9 \\ \times\ 6 \\ \hline \end{array}$$

㉝
$$\begin{array}{r} 8 \\ \times\ 9 \\ \hline \end{array}$$

㉞
$$\begin{array}{r} 0 \\ \times\ 9 \\ \hline \end{array}$$

㉟
$$\begin{array}{r} 1 \\ \times\ 8 \\ \hline \end{array}$$

㊱
$$\begin{array}{r} 0 \\ \times\ 6 \\ \hline \end{array}$$

㊲
$$\begin{array}{r} 1 \\ \times\ 7 \\ \hline \end{array}$$

㊳
$$\begin{array}{r} 1 \\ \times\ 5 \\ \hline \end{array}$$

㊴
$$\begin{array}{r} 9 \\ \times\ 3 \\ \hline \end{array}$$

㊵
$$\begin{array}{r} 8 \\ \times\ 4 \\ \hline \end{array}$$

㊶
$$\begin{array}{r} 0 \\ \times\ 2 \\ \hline \end{array}$$

㊷
$$\begin{array}{r} 9 \\ \times\ 5 \\ \hline \end{array}$$

㊸
$$\begin{array}{r} 0 \\ \times\ 7 \\ \hline \end{array}$$

㊹
$$\begin{array}{r} 1 \\ \times\ 6 \\ \hline \end{array}$$

㊺
$$\begin{array}{r} 8 \\ \times\ 7 \\ \hline \end{array}$$

Solve the problems. Show your work.

㊻ There are 9 apples in a basket.

How many apples are there in 6 baskets?

_____ = _____

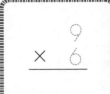
$$\begin{array}{r} 9 \\ \times\ 6 \\ \hline \end{array}$$

There are _____ apples.

㊼ How many wings do 9 frogs have?

_____ = _____

9 frogs have _____ wings.

㊽ How many tails do 7 dogs have?

_____ = _____

7 dogs have _____ tails.

㊾ Tom buys 3 boxes of pencils. Each box costs $8.

How much does Tom pay in all?

_____ = _____

Tom pays $ _____ in all.

Help Sally fill in the missing numbers so that the sum of the three numbers on each triangle is equal to 15.

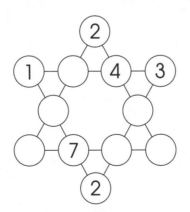

More Multiplying

1.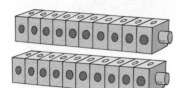

   2 groups of ten $= 2 \times 10$

   $= 20$

   $\begin{array}{r} 10 \\ \times\ \ 2 \\ \hline 20 \end{array}$

2.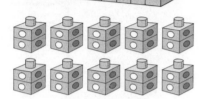

   10 groups of two $= 10 \times 2$

   $= 20$

   $\begin{array}{r} 2 \\ \times\ 10 \\ \hline 20 \end{array}$

Do the multiplication.

HINTS:

- When a number is multiplied by 10, you can get the product by adding a zero to the right of the number.

  e.g. $5 \times 10 = 10 \times 5 = 50$

  5 tens   10 fives   write a zero to the right of 5

  check 5 tens =

tens	ones
5	0

  = 50

① $\begin{array}{r} 10 \\ \times\ \ \ 3 \\ \hline \end{array}$

② $\begin{array}{r} 5 \\ \times\ 10 \\ \hline \end{array}$

③ $\begin{array}{r} 4 \\ \times\ 10 \\ \hline \end{array}$

④ $\begin{array}{r} 10 \\ \times\ \ \ 7 \\ \hline \end{array}$

⑤ $\begin{array}{r} 3 \\ \times\ \ 1 \\ \hline \end{array}$

⑥ $\begin{array}{r} 0 \\ \times\ \ 9 \\ \hline \end{array}$

⑦ $\begin{array}{r} 10 \\ \times\ \ \ 6 \\ \hline \end{array}$

⑧ $\begin{array}{r} 1 \\ \times\ 10 \\ \hline \end{array}$

⑨ $\begin{array}{r} 9 \\ \times\ 10 \\ \hline \end{array}$

⑩ $\begin{array}{r} 10 \\ \times\ \ \ 8 \\ \hline \end{array}$

⑪ $\begin{array}{r} 8 \\ \times\ \ 7 \\ \hline \end{array}$

⑫ $\begin{array}{r} 9 \\ \times\ \ 3 \\ \hline \end{array}$

⑬ $\begin{array}{r} 7 \\ \times\ \ 6 \\ \hline \end{array}$

⑭ $\begin{array}{r} 5 \\ \times\ \ 2 \\ \hline \end{array}$

Complete the following multiplication table.

⑮

×	1	2	3	4	5	6	7	8	9	10
1	1									
2		4								
3			9							
4				16						
5					25					
6						36				
7							49			
8								64		
9									81	
10										100

Find the flags for each child.   Write the letters on the flags.

A   6 x 2

B   5 x 6

C   4 x 3

D   4 x 4

E   3 x 10

F   8 x 2

⑯   ⑰   ⑱

Write 2 multiplication sentences for each picture.

⑲

⑳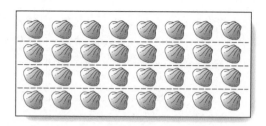

_____ X _____ = _____

_____ X _____ = _____

_____ X _____ = _____

_____ X _____ = _____

Complete the following multiplication sentences.

㉑ 7 X 6   = _____

㉒ 3 X 9   = _____

㉓ 8 X 5   = _____

㉔ 0 X 4   = _____

㉕ 9 X 1   = _____

㉖ 7 X 10   = _____

㉗ 5 X 9   = _____

㉘ 6 X 3   = _____

㉙ 9 X 8   = _____

㉚ 2 X 7   = _____

㉛ 2 X 0 X 5 = _____

㉜ 1 X 3 X 6 = _____

㉝ 3 X 3 X 10 = _____

㉞ 4 X 1 X 7 = _____

㉟ _____ X 7 = 7 X 3

        = _____

㊱ 8 X _____ = 2 X 4

        = _____

㊲ _____ X 4 = 2 X _____

        = 12

㊳ 5 X _____ = 0 X 7

        = _____

㊴ 4 X _____ = 5 X _____

        = 40

㊵ _____ X 2 = 5 X 4

        = _____

Solve the problems. Show your work.

㊶ How many legs do 10 snails have?

_____ = _____ _____ legs.

㊷ A ladybird has 6 legs. How many legs do 5 ladybirds have?

_____ = _____ _____ legs.

㊸ A butterfly has 4 wings. How many wings do 8 butterflies have?

_____ = _____ _____ wings.

㊹ There are 6 chocolate bars in a box. How many chocolate bars are there in 7 boxes?

_____ = _____ _____ bars.

㊺ There are 9 pears in a bag. How many pears are there in 4 bags?

_____ = _____ _____ pears.

㊻ Notebooks are sold for $3 each. Sally buys 7 notebooks. How much does she pay in all?

_____ = _____ $ _____.

Fill in the numbers to make each number sentence true.

① Use the same number in all boxes.

☐ + ☐ = ☐ × ☐

② The sum of three different numbers is equal to their product.

☐ + ☐ + ☐ = ☐ × ☐ × ☐

Introducing Division

There are 8 cakes. Put them on the plates in groups of 2. How many plates are needed?

Circle the cakes in groups of 2.

How many cakes are there?   8 cakes.

How many cakes in each group?   2 cakes.

How many groups are there?   4 groups.

There are 4 groups of two in 8.

4 plates are needed for 8 cakes with 2 cakes on each plate.

HINTS:

- Division is to share things equally into groups of the same size.

- " ÷ " means DIVIDE.

- Use a division sentence to represent division.

  e.g. 4 groups of two in eight is expressed as:

  $$8 ÷ 2 = 4$$
  dividend · divisor · quotient

Group the goodies and complete each statement.

①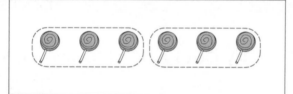

There are _____2_____ groups of three in 6.

②

There are _____ groups of four in 12.

③

There are _____ groups of five in 20.

④

There are _____ groups of two in 18.

⑤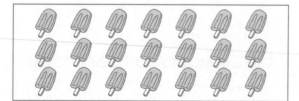

There are _____ groups of three in 21.

⑥

There are _____ groups of six in 24.

Help the children divide the stationery equally among themselves. Complete each statement.

⑦ Divide 18  equally among 3 children. Each child has _____  .

⑧ Divide 20  equally among 4 children. Each child has _____  .

⑨ Divide 30  equally among 5 children. Each child has _____  .

⑩ Divide 24  equally among 6 children. Each child has _____  .

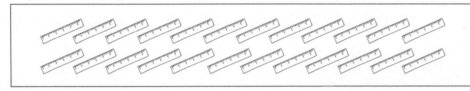

⑪ Divide 32  equally among 4 children. Each child has _____  .

⑫ Divide 32  equally among 6 children. Each child has _____  with _____  left over.

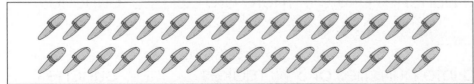

Aunt Mary has 24 boxes of juice. Fill in the blanks to show how she divides the juice equally among the children.

⑬ If each child gets 3 boxes, the juice can be shared among _____ children.

⑭ If each child gets 4 boxes, the juice can be shared among _____ children.

⑮ If each child gets 5 boxes, the juice can be shared among _____ children with _____ boxes left over.

Complete the division sentence for each picture.

⑯

Put 15 ☺ into 5 bunches. Each bunch has _____ ☺.

15 ÷ 5 = _____

15 ☺ divided into 5 bunches makes _____ ☺ in each bunch.

⑰
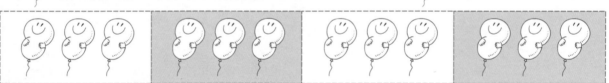

Put 12 ☺ into 4 bunches. Each bunch has _____ ☺.

12 ÷ 4 = _____

12 ☺ divided into 4 bunches makes _____ ☺ in each bunch.

⑱

Put 18 ☺ into bunches of 3 ☺. There are _____ bunches.

18 ÷ 3 = _____

18 ☺ divided into bunches of 3 ☺ makes _____ bunches.

Count and complete the division sentence for each picture.

⑲ ___6___ 🐜 divided into 2 equal groups.

___6___ ÷ ___2___ = _____

There are _____ 🐜 in each group.

⑳ _____ 🐞 divided into groups of 4.

_____ ÷ _____ = _____

There are _____ groups of 🐞.

㉑ _____ 🦋 divided into 3 equal groups.

_____ ÷ _____ = _____

There are _____ 🦋 in each group.

㉒ _____ 🐝 divided into groups of 5.

_____ ÷ _____ = _____

There are _____ groups of 🐝.

㉓ _____ 🦟 divided into groups of 3.

_____ ÷ _____ = _____

There are _____ groups of 🦟.

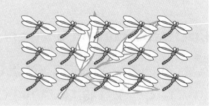

㉔ _____ 🦟 divided into 5 equal groups.

_____ ÷ _____ = _____

There are _____ 🦟 in each group.

Just for Fun

Fill in the missing numbers to continue the multiplication.

The number in each box is the product of the multiplication sentence on the left of ⟶.

① 2 x 3 ⟶ ☐ x 4 ⟶ ☐ x 0 ⟶ ☐

② 3 x 3 ⟶ ☐ x 5 ⟶ ☐ x 1 ⟶ ☐

Midway

Fill in the missing numbers.

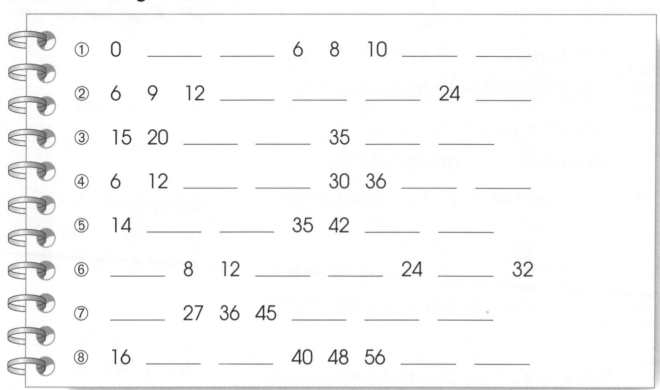

① 0 _____ _____ 6 8 10 _____ _____

② 6 9 12 _____ _____ _____ _____ 24 _____

③ 15 20 _____ _____ 35 _____ _____

④ 6 12 _____ _____ 30 36 _____ _____

⑤ 14 _____ _____ 35 42 _____ _____

⑥ _____ 8 12 _____ _____ 24 _____ 32

⑦ _____ 27 36 45 _____ _____ _____

⑧ 16 _____ _____ 40 48 56 _____ _____

Circle the correct answers.

⑨ When a number is multiplied by this number, the ones place of the product is always a 5 or a 0.

| 0 | 1 | 2 | 3 | 4 | 5 | 6 | 7 | 8 | 9 |

⑩ When a number is multiplied by this number, the product is the same as that number.

| 0 | 1 | 2 | 3 | 4 | 5 | 6 | 7 | 8 | 9 |

⑪ When a number is multiplied by this number, the product is always 0.

| 0 | 1 | 2 | 3 | 4 | 5 | 6 | 7 | 8 | 9 |

⑫ When a number is multiplied by any of these numbers, the product is always an even number.

| 0 | 1 | 2 | 3 | 4 | 5 | 6 | 7 | 8 | 9 |

Do the multiplication.

⑬
$$\begin{array}{r} 8 \\ \times\ 7 \\ \hline \end{array}$$

⑭
$$\begin{array}{r} 0 \\ \times\ 6 \\ \hline \end{array}$$

⑮
$$\begin{array}{r} 10 \\ \times\ 5 \\ \hline \end{array}$$

⑯
$$\begin{array}{r} 6 \\ \times\ 5 \\ \hline \end{array}$$

⑰
$$\begin{array}{r} 9 \\ \times\ 1 \\ \hline \end{array}$$

⑱
$$\begin{array}{r} 2 \\ \times\ 7 \\ \hline \end{array}$$

⑲
$$\begin{array}{r} 3 \\ \times\ 8 \\ \hline \end{array}$$

⑳
$$\begin{array}{r} 4 \\ \times\ 3 \\ \hline \end{array}$$

㉑
$$\begin{array}{r} 3 \\ \times\ 10 \\ \hline \end{array}$$

㉒
$$\begin{array}{r} 1 \\ \times\ 8 \\ \hline \end{array}$$

㉓
$$\begin{array}{r} 7 \\ \times\ 5 \\ \hline \end{array}$$

㉔
$$\begin{array}{r} 2 \\ \times\ 9 \\ \hline \end{array}$$

㉕
$$\begin{array}{r} 6 \\ \times\ 4 \\ \hline \end{array}$$

㉖
$$\begin{array}{r} 5 \\ \times\ 9 \\ \hline \end{array}$$

㉗
$$\begin{array}{r} 3 \\ \times\ 6 \\ \hline \end{array}$$

㉘
$$\begin{array}{r} 7 \\ \times\ 4 \\ \hline \end{array}$$

㉙ $2 \times 5 =$ _____

㉚ $3 \times 7 =$ _____

㉛ $9 \times 3 =$ _____

㉜ $8 \times 0 =$ _____

㉝ $5 \times 4 =$ _____

㉞ $2 \times 6 =$ _____

㉟ $7 \times 9 =$ _____

㊱ $1 \times 7 =$ _____

㊲ $4 \times 8 =$ _____

㊳ $9 \times 2 =$ _____

㊴ $3 \times 2 =$ _____

㊵ $8 \times 5 =$ _____

㊶ $8 \times 6 =$ _____

㊷ $9 \times 4 =$ _____

㊸ $6 \times 9 =$ _____

Complete the multiplication sentences.

㊽ _____ × 6 = 6

㊺ 3 × 4 × 0 = _____

㊽ 2 × 2 × 10 = _____

㊿ 4 × 8 = 8 × _____

          = _____

㊼ 5 × 0 = _____ × 9

          = _____

㊾ 8 × _____ = _____ × 4

          = 24

㊺ _____ × 7 = 0

㊽ 5 × 1 × 7 = _____

㊾ 1 × 6 × 9 = _____

㊿ _____ × 9 = 6 × 6

          = _____

㊼ _____ × 3 = 5 × _____

          = 30

㊾ 7 × _____ = 6 × 7

          = _____

In each group, put a X in the ◯ beside the number sentence that is different.

㊽
A. 4 eights ◯
B. 4 + 8 ◯
C. 8 + 8 + 8 + 8 ◯
D. 8 × 4 ◯

㊾
A. 5 zeros ◯
B. 0 × 5 ◯
C. 0 + 0 + 0 + 0 + 0 ◯
D. 1 × 5 ◯

㊿
A. 6 + 6 + 6 + 6 + 6 ◯
B. 6 × 5 ◯
C. 5 times 6 ◯
D. 5 + 5 + 5 + 5 + 5 ◯

㊾
A. 7 + 8 ◯
B. 7 × 8 ◯
C. 8 sevens ◯
D. 7 times 8 ◯

Count and complete the division sentence for each picture.

⑥⓪ _____ 🍭 divided into 4 equal groups.

_____ ÷ _____ = _____

There are _____ 🍭 in each group.

⑥① _____ 🍭 divided into groups of 3.

_____ ÷ _____ = _____

There are _____ groups of 3 🍭.

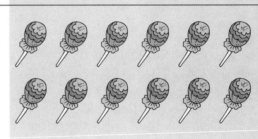

Solve the problems. Show your work.

⑥② Divide 6 bags of candy among 3 children. How many bags of candy does each child have?

_____ = _____   _____ bags of candy.

⑥③ A dragonfly has 4 wings. How many wings do 6 dragonflies have?

_____ = _____   _____ wings.

⑥④ A cupboard has 5 shelves with 8 cups on each shelf. How many cups are there in the cupboard ?

_____ = _____   _____ cups.

⑥⑤ A box of ice lollies costs $7. Sally buys 3 boxes for her birthday party. How much does Sally pay for the ice lollies ?

_____ = _____ $ _____.

⑥⑥ 4 children share a box of chocolates. Each child gets 3 chocolates. How many chocolates does each child get if the same box of chocolates is shared among 3 children?

Each child gets _____ chocolates.

Multiplication and Division Fact Families

EXAMPLES

1.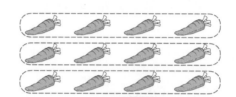
There are 4 groups of 3 🥕.
4 × 3 = 12
There are 12 🥕.

   Divide 12 🥕 into 4 groups.
12 ÷ 4 = 3
Each group has 3 🥕.

2. There are 3 groups of 4 🥕.
3 × 4 = 12
There are 12 🥕.

   Divide 12 🥕 into 3 groups.
12 ÷ 3 = 4
Each group has 4 🥕.

HINTS:

- Get familiar with the multiplication facts to be ready for division.

- There are 2 multiplication facts and 2 division facts for a fact family using the same 3 numbers.

  e.g.   3 × 5 = 15   15 ÷ 5 = 3
          5 × 3 = 15   15 ÷ 3 = 5

Look at the pictures. Complete the multiplication and division sentences.

①

_____ × 4 = 12   12 ÷ _____ = 4

②

_____ × 3 = 15   15 ÷ _____ = 3

③

_____ × 6 = 18   18 ÷ _____ = 6

④

_____ × 5 = 20   20 ÷ _____ = 5

⑤

_____ × 7 = 35   35 ÷ _____ = 7

⑥

_____ × 8 = 16   16 ÷ _____ = 8

⑦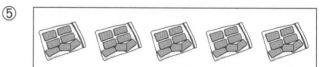

_____ × 3 = 12   12 ÷ _____ = 3

Write a fact family for each picture.

⑧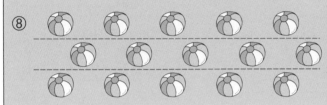

$\underline{\hspace{0.6cm}3\hspace{0.6cm}} \times \underline{\hspace{0.6cm}5\hspace{0.6cm}} = \underline{\hspace{0.8cm}}$

$\underline{\hspace{0.8cm}} \times \underline{\hspace{0.8cm}} = \underline{\hspace{0.8cm}}$

$\underline{\hspace{0.8cm}} \div \underline{\hspace{0.8cm}} = \underline{\hspace{0.8cm}}$

$\underline{\hspace{0.8cm}} \div \underline{\hspace{0.8cm}} = \underline{\hspace{0.8cm}}$

⑨

$\underline{\hspace{0.6cm}2\hspace{0.6cm}} \times \underline{\hspace{0.6cm}8\hspace{0.6cm}} = \underline{\hspace{0.8cm}}$

$\underline{\hspace{0.8cm}} \times \underline{\hspace{0.8cm}} = \underline{\hspace{0.8cm}}$

$\underline{\hspace{0.8cm}} \div \underline{\hspace{0.8cm}} = \underline{\hspace{0.8cm}}$

$\underline{\hspace{0.8cm}} \div \underline{\hspace{0.8cm}} = \underline{\hspace{0.8cm}}$

⑩

$\underline{\hspace{0.8cm}} \times \underline{\hspace{0.8cm}} = \underline{\hspace{0.8cm}}$

$\underline{\hspace{0.8cm}} \times \underline{\hspace{0.8cm}} = \underline{\hspace{0.8cm}}$

$\underline{\hspace{0.8cm}} \div \underline{\hspace{0.8cm}} = \underline{\hspace{0.8cm}}$

$\underline{\hspace{0.8cm}} \div \underline{\hspace{0.8cm}} = \underline{\hspace{0.8cm}}$

⑪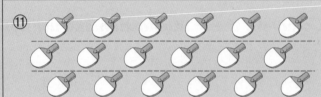

$\underline{\hspace{0.8cm}} \times \underline{\hspace{0.8cm}} = \underline{\hspace{0.8cm}}$

$\underline{\hspace{0.8cm}} \times \underline{\hspace{0.8cm}} = \underline{\hspace{0.8cm}}$

$\underline{\hspace{0.8cm}} \div \underline{\hspace{0.8cm}} = \underline{\hspace{0.8cm}}$

$\underline{\hspace{0.8cm}} \div \underline{\hspace{0.8cm}} = \underline{\hspace{0.8cm}}$

⑫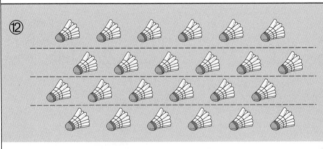

$\underline{\hspace{0.8cm}} \times \underline{\hspace{0.8cm}} = \underline{\hspace{0.8cm}}$

$\underline{\hspace{0.8cm}} \times \underline{\hspace{0.8cm}} = \underline{\hspace{0.8cm}}$

$\underline{\hspace{0.8cm}} \div \underline{\hspace{0.8cm}} = \underline{\hspace{0.8cm}}$

$\underline{\hspace{0.8cm}} \div \underline{\hspace{0.8cm}} = \underline{\hspace{0.8cm}}$

⑬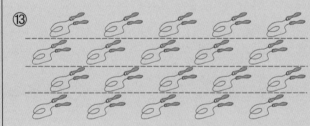

$\underline{\hspace{0.8cm}} \times \underline{\hspace{0.8cm}} = \underline{\hspace{0.8cm}}$

$\underline{\hspace{0.8cm}} \times \underline{\hspace{0.8cm}} = \underline{\hspace{0.8cm}}$

$\underline{\hspace{0.8cm}} \div \underline{\hspace{0.8cm}} = \underline{\hspace{0.8cm}}$

$\underline{\hspace{0.8cm}} \div \underline{\hspace{0.8cm}} = \underline{\hspace{0.8cm}}$

Find the quotients using multiplication facts.

⑭ 3 X 6   = 18   ⑮ 4 X 9   = 36   ⑯ 6 X 8   = 48

   18 ÷ 3   = _____   36 ÷ 9   = _____   48 ÷ 6   = _____

   18 ÷ 6   = _____   36 ÷ 4   = _____   48 ÷ 8   = _____

⑰ 7 X 4   = 28   ⑱ 8 X 3   = 24   ⑲ 5 X 7   = 35

   28 ÷ 4   = _____   24 ÷ 8   = _____   35 ÷ 5   = _____

   28 ÷ 7   = _____   24 ÷ 3   = _____   35 ÷ 7   = _____

Complete the multiplication and division sentences.

⑳ 6 X 9   = _____   ㉑ 8 X 5   = _____   ㉒ 4 X 8   = _____

   54 ÷ 6   = _____   40 ÷ 8   = _____   32 ÷ 8   = _____

㉓ 9 X 3   = _____   ㉔ 7 X 6   = _____   ㉕ 5 X 9   = _____

   27 ÷ 3   = _____   42 ÷ 7   = _____   45 ÷ 5   = _____

Fill in the missing numbers.

㉖ _____ X 4 = 16   ㉗ _____ X 5 = 30   ㉘ _____ X 2 = 14

   16 ÷ 4 = _____   30 ÷ 5 = _____   14 ÷ 2 = _____

㉙ 63 ÷ 7 = _____   ㉚ _____ X 3 = 9   ㉛ 48 ÷ 8 = _____

   7 X _____ = 63   9 ÷ 3 = _____   8 X _____ = 48

㉜ 81 ÷ 9 = _____   ㉝ _____ X 8 = 64   ㉞ 36 ÷ 6 = _____

   _____ X 9 = _____   64 ÷ 8 = _____   _____ X 6 = _____

Write the fact family for each group of numbers.

㉟ 7   8   56

_____ X _____ = _____

_____ X _____ = _____

_____ ÷ _____ = _____

_____ ÷ _____ = _____

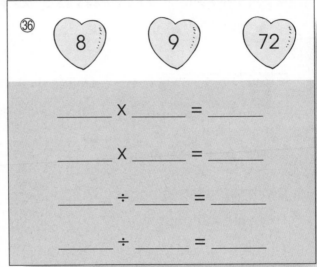

㊱ 8   9   72

_____ X _____ = _____

_____ X _____ = _____

_____ ÷ _____ = _____

_____ ÷ _____ = _____

Write a multiplication sentence and a division sentence for each statement.

㊲ There are 12 cakes in all. Put 2 cakes on a plate. There are 6 plates of cakes.

_____ X _____ = _____   _____ ÷ _____ = _____

㊳ There are 40 stickers in all. Put 5 stickers on a page. There are 8 pages of stickers.

_____ X _____ = _____   _____ ÷ _____ = _____

㊴ There are 30 children in all. Group 6 children into a team. There are 5 teams of children.

_____ X _____ = _____   _____ ÷ _____ = _____

㊵ $45 is shared equally among 5 children. Each child gets $9.

_____ X _____ = _____   _____ ÷ _____ = _____

Just for Fun

Complete the square.

Write the numbers from 1 to 7 in the boxes to make the number sentence on each side of the square true.

8	–		=	
÷				+
=				=
	X		=	

Dividing by 1, 2 or 3

1.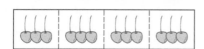

Divide 8 into groups of 2.

There are 4 groups of . $8 \div 2 = 4$

2.

Divide 12 🍒 into groups of 3.

There are 4 groups of 🍒 .

$12 \div 3 = 4$

Count and complete the division sentence to match each picture.

①

___12___ $\div\ 3 =$ ___4___

②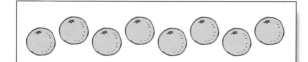

_____ $\div\ 2 =$ _____

HINTS:

- Division facts can be written in two different ways.

  e.g. $12 \div 3 = 4$ or $3\overline{)12}$ ← align the numbers on the right hand side

- Do the division by recalling the multiplication facts.

  e.g. $12 \div 3 = ?$

  recall $3 \times 4 = 12$

  so $12 \div 3 = 4$

- Any number divided by 1 will stay the same.

③

_____ $\div\ 1 =$ _____

④

_____ $\div\ 2 =$ _____

⑤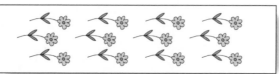

_____ $\div\ 3 =$ _____

⑥

_____ $\div\ 2 =$ _____

⑦

_____ $\div\ 1 =$ _____

⑧

_____ $\div\ 3 =$ _____

Find the quotients using multiplication facts. Fill in the missing numbers.

⑨ ÷ 2 → [ ]
10
← 2 ×

[ ] × 2 = 10

10 ÷ 2 = [ ]

⑩ ÷ 3 → [ ]
18
← 3 ×

[ ] × 3 = 18

18 ÷ 3 = [ ]

⑪ ÷ 1 → [ ]
9
← 1 ×

[ ] × 1 = 9

9 ÷ 1 = [ ]

⑫ ÷ 2 → [ ]
14
← 2 ×

[ ] × 2 = 14

14 ÷ 2 = [ ]

Find the quotients. Fill in the missing numbers.

⑬
```
    [8]
2 ) 1 6
    1 6
```

⑭
```
    [  ]
3 ) 2 1
    2 1
```

⑮
```
    [  ]
1 ) 8
    8
```

⑯
```
    [  ]
3 ) 1 2
    [  ]
```

⑰
```
    [  ]
1 ) 6
    [  ]
```

⑱
```
    [  ]
2 ) 1 8
    [  ]
```

⑲
```
    [  ]
1 ) 7
    [  ]
```

⑳
```
    [  ]
2 ) 6
    [  ]
```

㉑
```
    [  ]
3 ) 2 7
    [  ]
```

Do the division.

㉒ $24 \div 3 =$ ______	㉓ $16 \div 2 =$ ______	㉔ $4 \div 2 =$ ______
㉕ $10 \div 1 =$ ______	㉖ $12 \div 3 =$ ______	㉗ $9 \div 3 =$ ______
㉘ $12 \div 2 =$ ______	㉙ $4 \div 1 =$ ______	㉚ $2 \div 1 =$ ______
㉛ $18 \div 2 =$ ______	㉜ $18 \div 3 =$ ______	㉝ $6 \div 3 =$ ______
㉞ $2 \div 2 =$ ______	㉟ $3 \div 1 =$ ______	㊱ $15 \div 3 =$ ______
㊲ $3 \div 3 =$ ______	㊳ $5 \div 1 =$ ______	㊴ $10 \div 2 =$ ______
㊵ $3 \overline{)12}$	㊶ $2 \overline{)8}$	㊷ $1 \overline{)4}$
㊸ $2 \overline{)14}$	㊹ $3 \overline{)9}$	㊺ $3 \overline{)21}$
㊻ $3 \overline{)27}$	㊼ $1 \overline{)8}$	㊽ $2 \overline{)16}$
㊾ $1 \overline{)3}$	㊿ $2 \overline{)6}$	(51) $3 \overline{)6}$

Solve the problems. Show your work.

52. Mom divides a box of 24 chocolates among Tom and his 2 sisters. How many chocolates does each child have?

$$\underline{\hspace{2cm}} \div \underline{\hspace{2cm}} = \underline{\hspace{2cm}}$$

Each child has _____ chocolates.

$3\overline{)24}$

53. Tom has 16 balloons. He ties 2 balloons together in a bunch. How many bunches of balloons are there ?

$$\underline{\hspace{2cm}} \div \underline{\hspace{2cm}} = \underline{\hspace{2cm}}$$

There are _____ bunches of balloons.

54. Sally cuts 6 flowers from the garden. She puts 1 flower in each vase. How many vases does Sally need?

$$\underline{\hspace{2cm}} \div \underline{\hspace{2cm}} = \underline{\hspace{2cm}}$$

She needs _____ vases.

55. Tom and Sally share 12 lollipops between them. How many lollipops does each child have?

$$\underline{\hspace{2cm}} \div \underline{\hspace{2cm}} = \underline{\hspace{2cm}}$$

Each child has _____ lollipops.

Just for Fun

How many soldiers?

A number of soldiers are lining up in front of the Parliament Building. One soldier is holding a flag and the others are each holding a gun. Counting from the left, the 7th soldier is holding a flag. Counting from the right, the 10th soldier is holding a flag. How many soldiers are there in all?

_____ soldiers.

Dividing by 4 or 5

1.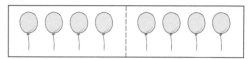

8 ⚬ divided into groups of 4.

There are 2 groups of ⚬. $8 \div 4 = 2$

2.

15 ⚬ divided into groups of 5.

There are 3 groups of ⚬.

$15 \div 5 = 3$

Count and complete the division sentence to match each picture.

HINTS:

- Align the quotient on the right hand side.

$$5\overline{)15} \quad \frac{3}{15} \quad X \qquad 5\overline{)15} \quad \frac{3}{15} \quad ✓$$

- Dividing a number with 0 at the ones place by 5, the quotient is always an even number. Dividing a number with 5 at the ones place by 5, the quotient is always an odd number.

e.g. $10 \div 5 = 2$ ← quotient is an even number

  0 at the ones place

    $35 \div 5 = 7$ ← quotient is an odd number

  5 at the ones place

①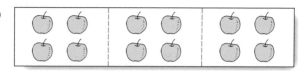

    _12_ ÷ 4 = _3_

②

    _____ ÷ 5 = _____

③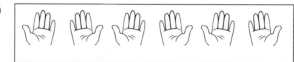

    _____ ÷ 5 = _____

④

    _____ ÷ 4 = _____

⑤

    _____ ÷ 4 = _____

⑥

    _____ ÷ 5 = _____

⑦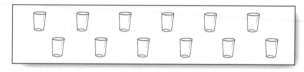

    _____ ÷ 4 = _____

Complete the multiplication table and use the multiplication facts to find the quotients.

⑧

◩	1	2	3	4	5	6	7	8	9
4			12						
5					25		35		

⑨ $10 \div 5 =$ _____   ⑩ $16 \div 4 =$ _____   ⑪ $12 \div 4 =$ _____

⑫ $32 \div 4 =$ _____   ⑬ $24 \div 4 =$ _____   ⑭ $20 \div 5 =$ _____

⑮ $40 \div 5 =$ _____   ⑯ $35 \div 5 =$ _____   ⑰ $36 \div 4 =$ _____

⑱ $20 \div 4 =$ _____   ⑲ $45 \div 5 =$ _____   ⑳ $28 \div 4 =$ _____

㉑ $30 \div 5 =$ _____   ㉒ $4 \div 4 =$ _____   ㉓ $15 \div 5 =$ _____

㉔ $5 \div 5 =$ _____   ㉕ $25 \div 5 =$ _____   ㉖ $8 \div 4 =$ _____

㉗ $4\overline{)16}$ ㉘ $5\overline{)30}$ ㉙ $4\overline{)20}$

㉚ $5\overline{)45}$ ㉛ $4\overline{)32}$ ㉜ $5\overline{)25}$

㉝ $4\overline{)36}$ ㉞ $5\overline{)40}$ ㉟ $4\overline{)24}$

Match the division sentences with the quotients.

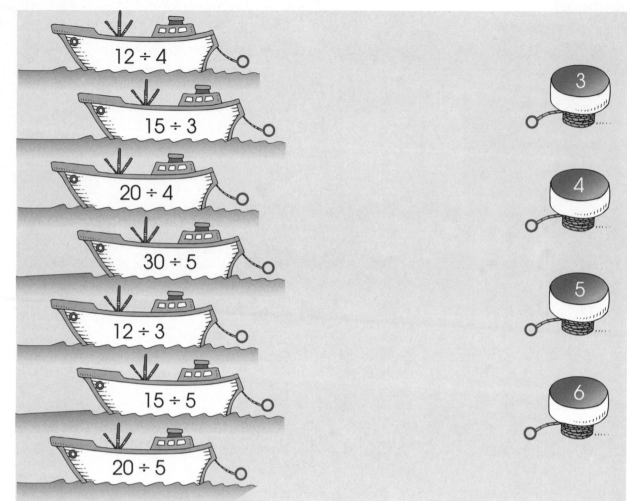

Fill in the boxes.

③⑦ ☐ ÷ 4 = 2

③⑧ 32 ÷ ☐ = 4

③⑨ ☐ ÷ 5 = 7

④⓪ 40 ÷ ☐ = 8

④① ☐ ÷ 5 = 4

④② 36 ÷ ☐ = 9

④③ ☐ ÷ 4 = 8

④④ 45 ÷ ☐ = 9

④⑤ ☐ ÷ 5 = 3

④⑥ ☐ ÷ 4 = 6

④⑦ ☐ ÷ 5 = 5

④⑧ 28 ÷ ☐ = 7

④⑨

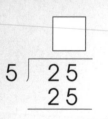

⑤⓪

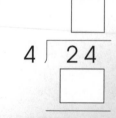

⑤①

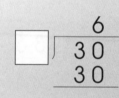

Solve the problems. Show your work.

(52) Dad plants 30 roses in 5 rows in the garden. How many roses are there in each row?

______ ÷ ______ = ______

There are ______ roses in each row.

(53) Tom buys 36 goldfish. He puts them in 4 bowls. How many goldfish are there in each bowl?

______ ÷ ______ = ______

There are ______ goldfish in each bowl.

(54) A chicken pie costs $4. How many chicken pies can be bought for $28?

______ ÷ ______ = ______

______ chicken pies can be bought.

(55) 20 boys and girls went to the movies in 5 cars. How many children were there in each car?

______ ÷ ______ = ______

______ children were in each car.

Put + or – in the ◯ to make each number sentence true.

① 4 ◯ 3 ◯ 1 ◯ 2 = 0

② 4 ◯ 3 ◯ 2 ◯ 1 = 2

③ 4 ◯ 3 ◯ 2 ◯ 1 = 4

④ 4 ◯ 3 ◯ 2 ◯ 1 = 6

⑤ 4 ◯ 3 ◯ 2 ◯ 1 = 8

⑥ 4 ◯ 3 ◯ 2 ◯ 1 = 10

Dividing by 6 or 7

E X A M P L E S

1.

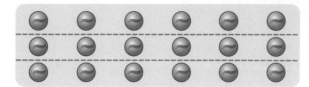

Divide 18 ⬤ into groups of 6.

There are 3 groups of ⬤. $18 \div 6 = 3$

2.

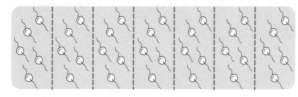

Divide 35 🐚 into 7 groups. Each group has 5 🐚 .

$35 \div 7 = 5$

INTS:

- Check your answers by using multiplication facts.

  e.g. $35 \div 7 = 6$ ✗

  check : $6 \times 7 = 42$

  not equal to the dividend 35 so 6 is the wrong answer

  $35 \div 7 = 5$ ✓

  check : $5 \times 7 = 35$

  so 5 is the correct answer

Complete the division sentence for each picture. Then check your answers by using multiplication.

①

_24_ ÷ 6 = _4_

check _4_ X 6 = _24_

②

_____ ÷ 7 = _____

check _____ X 7 = _____

③

_____ ÷ 6 = _____

check _____ X 6 = _____

④
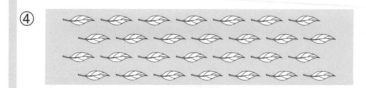

_____ ÷ 7 = _____

check _____ X 7 = _____

Do the division and check your answers using multiplication facts.

⑤ $63 \div 7 =$ _____

check

$7 \times$ _____ $= 63$

⑥ $36 \div 6 =$ _____

check

$6 \times$ _____ $= 36$

⑦ $49 \div 7 =$ _____

check

$7 \times$ _____ $= 49$

⑧ $54 \div 6 =$ _____

check

_____

⑨ $42 \div 7 =$ _____

check

_____

⑩ $24 \div 6 =$ _____

check

_____

⑪ $28 \div 7 =$ _____

check

_____

⑫ $30 \div 6 =$ _____

check

_____

⑬ $21 \div 7 =$ _____

check

_____

⑭ $18 \div 6 =$ _____

check

_____

⑮ $14 \div 7 =$ _____

check

_____

⑯ $48 \div 6 =$ _____

check

_____

Find the quotients.

⑰ $12 \div 6 =$ _____

⑱ $35 \div 7 =$ _____

⑲ $42 \div 6 =$ _____

⑳ $7 \div 7 =$ _____

㉑ $6 \div 6 =$ _____

㉒ $56 \div 7 =$ _____

㉓

$6 \overline{)36}$

㉔

$7 \overline{)21}$

㉕

$7 \overline{)49}$

㉖

$7 \overline{)28}$

㉗

$6 \overline{)54}$

㉘

$6 \overline{)18}$

Check the division sentences. Put a ✓ if the division sentence is true. Put a ✗ if the answer is wrong and write down the correct quotient.

	Division sentence	✓ or ✗	Correct quotient
㉙	$48 \div 6 = 8$		
㉚	$40 \div 5 = 6$		
㉛	$56 \div 7 = 8$		
㉜	$42 \div 7 = 9$		
㉝	$45 \div 5 = 9$		
㉞	$32 \div 4 = 7$		

Fill in the boxes.

㉟ $\boxed{} \div 5 = 6$ ㊱ $49 \div \boxed{} = 7$ ㊲ $\boxed{} \div 6 = 8$

㊳ $\boxed{} \div 7 = 3$ ㊴ $54 \div \boxed{} = 9$ ㊵ $28 \div \boxed{} = 4$

㊶ $36 \div \boxed{} = 6$ ㊷ $\boxed{} \div 7 = 8$ ㊸ $42 \div \boxed{} = 6$

㊹ $63 \div \boxed{} = 9$ ㊺ $\boxed{} \div 6 = 5$ ㊻ $\boxed{} \div 6 = 9$

㊼ $35 \div \boxed{} = 5$ ㊽ $14 \div \boxed{} = 2$ ㊾ $21 \div \boxed{} = 3$

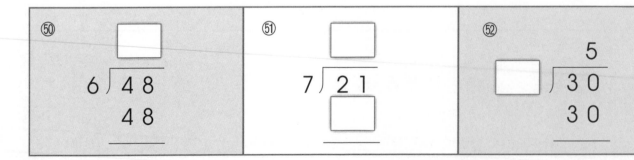

Solve the problems. Show your work and check your answers.

53   There are 54 soldiers lining up in 6 rows.

     How many soldiers are there in each row?

     _____ ÷ _____ = _____

     There are _____ soldiers in each row.

check

54   Divide 56 marbles among 7 children.

     How many marbles does each child have?

     _____ ÷ _____ = _____

     Each child has _____ marbles.

check

55   Sally cuts 24 tulips from the garden and puts them equally in 6 vases.

     How many tulips does Sally put in each vase?

     _____ ÷ _____ = _____

     Sally puts _____ tulips in each vase.

check

56   Mom pays $35 for the sausage rolls at $7 each box. How many boxes of sausage rolls does Mom buy?

     _____ ÷ _____ = _____

     Mom buys _____ boxes of sausage rolls.

check

Colour the two clocks that show the time Tom goes to bed and wakes up.

Ah! I've just slept for 2 hours.

  A   B   C   D   E

13 Dividing by 8 or 9

1.

$36 \div 9 = 4$

$36 \div 4 = 9$

$$9\overline{)\begin{array}{c} 4 \\ 3\ 6 \\ \end{array}}$$
$$3\ 6$$

2.

$24 \div 8 = 3$

$24 \div 3 = 8$

$$8\overline{)\begin{array}{c} 3 \\ 2\ 4 \\ \end{array}}$$
$$2\ 4$$

HINTS:

- Dividing 0 by any numbers always gives zero.

  so $0 \div 8 = 0$

  or $0 \div 9 = 0$

- 2 division sentences can be written for each picture.

  e.g. Divide 36 cubes into 4 groups. Each group has 9 cubes.

  $36 \div 4 = 9$

  Divide 36 cubes into groups of 9. There are 4 groups.

  $36 \div 9 = 4$

Complete two division sentences to match each picture.

①

$27 \div \underline{\quad 3 \quad} = \underline{\quad\quad}$

$27 \div \underline{\quad 9 \quad} = \underline{\quad\quad}$

②

$32 \div \underline{\quad\quad} = \underline{\quad\quad}$

$32 \div \underline{\quad\quad} = \underline{\quad\quad}$

③

$\underline{\quad\quad} \div \underline{\quad\quad} = \underline{\quad\quad}$

$\underline{\quad\quad} \div \underline{\quad\quad} = \underline{\quad\quad}$

④

$\underline{\quad\quad} \div \underline{\quad\quad} = \underline{\quad\quad}$

$\underline{\quad\quad} \div \underline{\quad\quad} = \underline{\quad\quad}$

Complete the division sentences.

⑤ $72 \div 9 = $ _____

$72 \div$ _____ $= 9$

⑥ $64 \div 8 = $ _____

$64 \div$ _____ $= 8$

⑦ $32 \div 8 = $ _____

$32 \div$ _____ $= 8$

⑧ $45 \div 9 = $ _____

$45 \div$ _____ $= 9$

⑨ $36 \div 9 = $ _____

$36 \div$ _____ $= 9$

⑩ $56 \div 8 = $ _____

$56 \div$ _____ $= 8$

⑪ $24 \div 8 = $ _____

$24 \div$ _____ $= 8$

⑫ $16 \div 8 = $ _____

$16 \div$ _____ $= 8$

⑬ $27 \div 9 = $ _____

$27 \div$ _____ $= 9$

⑭ $40 \div 8 = $ _____

$40 \div$ _____ $= 8$

⑮ $18 \div 9 = $ _____

$18 \div$ _____ $= 9$

⑯ $54 \div 9 = $ _____

$54 \div$ _____ $= 9$

⑰ $9 \div 9 = $ _____

$9 \div$ _____ $= 9$

⑱ $48 \div 8 = $ _____

$48 \div$ _____ $= 8$

⑲ $72 \div 8 = $ _____

$72 \div$ _____ $= 8$

⑳ $63 \div 9 = $ _____

$63 \div$ _____ $= 9$

㉑ $81 \div 9 = $ _____

$81 \div$ _____ $= 9$

㉒ $8 \div 8 = $ _____

$8 \div$ _____ $= 8$

㉓ $8 \overline{)16}$

㉔ $8 \overline{)72}$

㉕ $9 \overline{)36}$

㉖ $9 \overline{)54}$

㉗ $9 \overline{)45}$

㉘ $8 \overline{)64}$

㉙ $8 \overline{)56}$

㉚ $9 \overline{)81}$

㉛ $8 \overline{)32}$

Match the division sentences on the toys with the quotients that the children are holding. Write the representing letters in the spaces.

③② [child holding 3] □ □ □ □

③③ [child holding 8] □ □ □ □

③④ [child holding 9] □ □ □ □

A $16 \div 2$

B $3 \overline{)27}$

C $72 \div 8$

D $72 \div 9$

E $6 \overline{)18}$

F $9 \overline{)27}$

G $15 \div 5$

H $4 \overline{)32}$

I $24 \div 8$

J $18 \div 2$

K $45 \div 5$

L $3 \overline{)24}$

Solve the problems. Show your work.

㉟ 9 children shared a box of 54 chocolates equally among them. How many chocolates did each child get?

_____ ÷ _____ = _____

Each child got _____ chocolates.

㊱ Sally bought 8 sketch books for $56. How much did each sketch book cost?

_____ ÷ _____ = _____

Each sketch book cost $ _____ .

㊲ The school music room has 45 seats arranged in rows of 9. How many rows of seats are there in the music room?

_____ ÷ _____ = _____

There are _____ rows of seats in the music room.

Help Sally use the number cards to form the following numbers. You need not use all the cards each time.

① A 2-digit number closest to 100 ☐

② A 3-digit number closest to 100 ☐

③ The number closest to 1000 ☐

④ The number closest to 500 ☐

Division with Remainders

Divide 30 pencils equally among 7 children.
How many pencils does each child have?
How many pencils are left over?

30 ÷ 7
= 4 with 2 left over
= 4R2

```
      4 R2
7 ) 3 0
    2 8
      2
```

Each child has 4 pencils.
2 pencils are left over.

HINTS:

- Use multiplication facts to do division.

  e.g. 30 ÷ 7 = ?

  Think: 7 x 4 = 28
  7 x 5 = 35

  7 multiplied by 4 is closest to but not greater than 30.

  so
  ```
          4  ←——— quotient
  7 )  3 0  ←——— align the numbers on
      2 8         the right hand side
        2  ←——— 30 – 28 = 2 left over
  ```

  Write : 30 ÷ 7 = 4R2   or
  ```
              4 R 2
  quotient    7 ) 3 0
                  2 8
  remainder ——→    2
  ```

Circle and write a division sentence to match each picture.

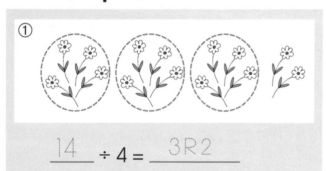

① ____14____ ÷ 4 = ____3R2____

② _____ ÷ 3 = _____

③ _____ ÷ 8 = _____

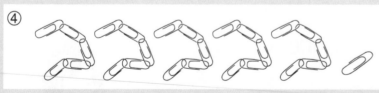

④ _____ ÷ 5 = _____

⑤ _____ ÷ 6 = _____

Do the division.

⑥ $25 \div 4 =$ _____ R _____

⑦ $40 \div 7 =$ _____ R _____

⑧ $80 \div 9 =$ _____

⑨ $26 \div 8 =$ _____

⑩ $35 \div 4 =$ _____

⑪ $27 \div 5 =$ _____

⑫ $44 \div 7 =$ _____

⑬ $41 \div 8 =$ _____

⑭ $17 \div 2 =$ _____

⑮ $51 \div 9 =$ _____

⑯ $39 \div 5 =$ _____

⑰ $22 \div 3 =$ _____

⑱ $9 \overline{)2\ 5}$

⑲ $3 \overline{)1\ 9}$

⑳ $5 \overline{)4\ 6}$

㉑ $6 \overline{)5\ 5}$

㉒ $7 \overline{)5\ 2}$

㉓ $4 \overline{)3\ 8}$

㉔ $8 \overline{)7\ 9}$

㉕ $6 \overline{)3\ 9}$

㉖ $3 \overline{)1\ 9}$

Fill in the boxes in ㊷ with letters representing the division sentences with 1 left over. Write the letters in sequence and help Tom find the key to open his box.

㉗ $3\overline{)17}$ m	㉘ $7\overline{)22}$ c	㉙ $4\overline{)38}$ s
㉚ $9\overline{)55}$ u	㉛ $6\overline{)44}$ i	㉜ $8\overline{)65}$ p
㉝ $5\overline{)26}$ b	㉞ $2\overline{)19}$ o	㉟ $3\overline{)29}$ v
㊱ $6\overline{)53}$ y	㊲ $4\overline{)13}$ a	㊳ $7\overline{)53}$ l
㊴ $8\overline{)38}$ k	㊵ $9\overline{)46}$ r	㊶ $5\overline{)41}$ d

㊷   The key is in the ⬚⬚⬚⬚⬚⬚⬚⬚⬚ .

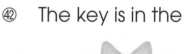

Solve the problems. Show your work.

㊸ 20 cakes on the table are arranged in rows of 6. How many rows of cakes are there on the table? How many cakes are left over?

_____ = _____

There are _____ row of cakes on the table. _____ cakes are left over.

㊹ 12 hot dogs are shared among 5 children. How many hot dogs does each child get? How many hot dogs are left over?

_____ = _____

Each child gets _____ hot dogs. _____ hot dogs are left over.

㊺ 89 books are put in a cupboard with 9 shelves. How many books are there on each shelf? How many books are left over?

_____ = _____

There are _____ books on each shelf. _____ books are left over.

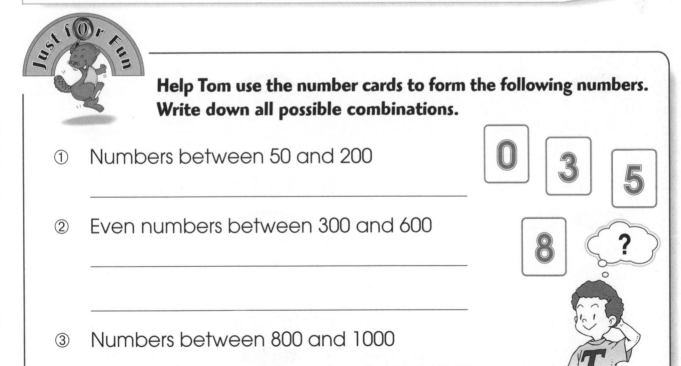

Just for Fun

Help Tom use the number cards to form the following numbers. Write down all possible combinations.

① Numbers between 50 and 200

_____

② Even numbers between 300 and 600

_____

_____

③ Numbers between 800 and 1000

_____

15 More Dividing

Divide 26 lollipops among 4 children.
How many lollipops does each child have?
How many lollipops are left over?

$26 \div 4 = 6R2$

Each child has 6 lollipops.
2 lollipops are left over.

check $6 \times 4 = 24$
          $24 + 2 = 26$

$$\begin{array}{r} 6 \\ 4 \overline{\smash{)}26} \\ 24 \\ \hline 2 \end{array}$$

HINTS:

- Use multiplication and addition to check the answer of division with left overs.

  e.g. $16 \div 3 = 5R1$

  check   quotient
            ↓   ┌─── divisor
            $5 \times 3 = 15$
            $15 + 1 = 16$ ←──── dividend
                └── remainder

- Add the remainder to the product of quotient and divisor will give the dividend.

Do the division and check your answers.

① $27 \div 6 = \underline{\quad 4R3 \quad}$

   check $\underline{\quad 4 \quad} \times 6 = \underline{\qquad}$

   $\underline{\qquad} + \underline{\quad 3 \quad} = 27$

② $19 \div 3 = \underline{\qquad}$

   check $\underline{\hspace{4cm}}$

   $\underline{\hspace{4cm}}$

③ $45 \div 7 = \underline{\qquad}$

   check $\underline{\hspace{4cm}}$

   $\underline{\hspace{4cm}}$

④ $39 \div 5 = \underline{\qquad}$

   check $\underline{\hspace{4cm}}$

   $\underline{\hspace{4cm}}$

⑤ $43 \div 5 = \underline{\qquad}$

   check $\underline{\hspace{4cm}}$

   $\underline{\hspace{4cm}}$

⑥ $70 \div 9 = \underline{\qquad}$

   check $\underline{\hspace{4cm}}$

   $\underline{\hspace{4cm}}$

⑦ $25 \div 4 = \underline{\qquad}$

   check $\underline{\hspace{4cm}}$

   $\underline{\hspace{4cm}}$

⑧ $15 \div 2 = \underline{\qquad}$

   check $\underline{\hspace{4cm}}$

   $\underline{\hspace{4cm}}$

Do the division.

⑨
$$9 \overline{)73}$$

⑩
$$4 \overline{)28}$$

⑪
$$5 \overline{)15}$$

⑫
$$3 \overline{)26}$$

⑬
$$6 \overline{)39}$$

⑭
$$8 \overline{)48}$$

⑮
$$2 \overline{)18}$$

⑯
$$7 \overline{)29}$$

⑰
$$4 \overline{)34}$$

⑱
$$5 \overline{)29}$$

⑲
$$3 \overline{)18}$$

⑳
$$9 \overline{)40}$$

㉑
$$6 \overline{)48}$$

㉒
$$8 \overline{)34}$$

㉓
$$2 \overline{)11}$$

㉔
$$7 \overline{)35}$$

㉕
$$4 \overline{)22}$$

㉖
$$5 \overline{)47}$$

Help Little Bear go to his mother following the path of correct answers. Draw the path.

㉗

11 ÷ 5 = 2R2

54 ÷ 9 = 7

18 ÷ 4 = 4R2

36 ÷ 6 = 6

27 ÷ 7 = 3R6

27 ÷ 9 = 4

32 ÷ 4 = 9

54 ÷ 9 = 6

21 ÷ 3 = 7

13 ÷ 2 = 6R1

42 ÷ 6 = 7

35 ÷ 8 = 4R3

48 ÷ 5 = 9R2

56 ÷ 7 = 9

27 ÷ 3 = 9

45 ÷ 9 = 5

Answer the questions. Write the division sentence and put a ✓ in the box if there are remainders.

㉘ Divide 24 candies equally among 8 children.

㉙ 46 cookies are shared among 5 children.

㉚ Put 30 stickers in rows of 6.

㉛ Divide 56 baseball cards among 8 children.

㉜ Arrange 27 chairs in rows of 9.

㉝ Fill 26 bottles in 4 six-pack cartons.

㉞ Tie 38 pencils into bunches of 7 pencils.

Just for Fun

Write 1 to 6 in the boxes to make the addition sentence and multiplication sentence true. You cannot use any numbers twice.

☐ + ☐ = ☐

☐ x ☐ = ☐

More Multiplying and Dividing

EXAMPLES

1. Arrange 35 stamps in rows of 5. How many rows are there?

   $35 \div 5 = 7$

   There are 7 rows.

2. There are 5 rows of stamps with 7 stamps in each row. How many stamps are there in all?

   $5 \times 7 = 35$

   There are 35 stamps in all.

HINTS:

- Read the problem carefully to see whether to use multiplication or division.

- Recall the fact families relating multiplication and division.

  e.g.
  $$9 \times 8 = 72$$
  $$8 \times 9 = 72$$
  changing the order of multiplication gives the same product
  $$72 \div 8 = 9$$
  $$72 \div 9 = 8$$

Do the multiplication or division.

①
$$\begin{array}{r} 0 \\ \times\ 8 \\ \hline \end{array}$$

②
$$\begin{array}{r} 7 \\ \times\ 6 \\ \hline \end{array}$$

③ $7\overline{)56}$

④ $4\overline{)36}$

⑤ $3\overline{)18}$

⑥ $6\overline{)48}$

⑦ $5\overline{)35}$

⑧ $9\overline{)63}$

⑨ $2\overline{)12}$

⑩ $8\overline{)72}$

⑪
$$\begin{array}{r} 5 \\ \times\ 2 \\ \hline \end{array}$$

⑫
$$\begin{array}{r} 3 \\ \times\ 0 \\ \hline \end{array}$$

⑬
$$\begin{array}{r} 10 \\ \times\ 5 \\ \hline \end{array}$$

⑭
$$\begin{array}{r} 1 \\ \times\ 9 \\ \hline \end{array}$$

Write a family of facts for each picture.

⑮

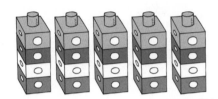

a.   5   x   4   = _____

b. _____ x _____ = _____

c. _____ ÷   5   = _____

d. _____ ÷   4   = _____

⑯

a. _____ x _____ = _____

b. _____ x _____ = _____

c. _____ ÷ _____ = _____

d. _____ ÷ _____ = _____

⑰

a. _____ x _____ = _____

b. _____ x _____ = _____

c. _____ ÷ _____ = _____

d. _____ ÷ _____ = _____

⑱

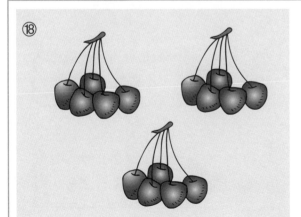

a. _____ x _____ ′= _____

b. _____ x _____ = _____

c. _____ ÷ _____ = _____

d. _____ ÷ _____ = _____

Match the multiplication sentence and division sentence in the same family of facts.

19. $18 \div 6 = 3$ ●

20. $28 \div 7 = 4$ ●

21. $56 \div 7 = 8$ ●

22. $20 \div 4 = 5$ ●

23. $21 \div 3 = 7$ ●

24. $32 \div 4 = 8$ ●

25. $30 \div 6 = 5$ ●

26. $48 \div 8 = 6$ ●

27. $45 \div 5 = 9$ ●

● A $7 \times 8 = 56$

● B $3 \times 7 = 21$

● C $3 \times 6 = 18$

● D $7 \times 4 = 28$

● E $4 \times 5 = 20$

● F $6 \times 5 = 30$

● G $9 \times 5 = 45$

● H $4 \times 8 = 32$

● I $6 \times 8 = 48$

Solve the problems. Show your work.

㉘ Mom bought 3 pizzas for Sally's birthday party. Each pizza was then divided into 8 pieces. How many pieces of pizza were there in all?

_____ = _____

There were _____ pieces of pizza in all.

㉙ Mom divided the birthday cake into 12 pieces. The cake was shared among Sally and 5 friends. How many pieces of cake did each child have?

_____ = _____

Each child had _____ pieces of cake.

㉚ Mom made 4 different kinds of sandwiches. There were 8 sandwiches in each kind. How many sandwiches did Mom make in all?

_____ = _____

Mom made _____ sandwiches.

㉛ Five children shared equally a box of 28 lollipops. Sally got all the leftovers. How many lollipops did Sally get?

_____ = _____

Sally got _____ lollipops.

Just for Fun

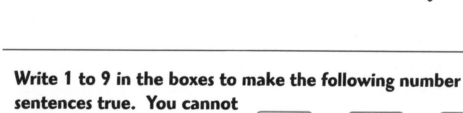

Write 1 to 9 in the boxes to make the following number sentences true. You cannot use any numbers twice.

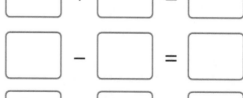

$$\boxed{} + \boxed{} = \boxed{}$$

$$\boxed{} - \boxed{} = \boxed{}$$

$$\boxed{} \times \boxed{} = \boxed{}$$

Fill in the missing numbers.

①   10   15   _____   25   _____   _____   _____

②   18   _____   36   45   _____   _____   _____

③   18   16   _____   12   _____   _____   _____

④   36   32   _____   _____   20   _____   _____

⑤   _____   64   56   _____   40   _____   _____

Find the answers.

⑥ $36 \div 9 =$ _____   ⑦ $45 \div 5 =$ _____   ⑧ $64 \div 8 =$ _____

⑨ $4 \times 7 =$ _____   ⑩ $6 \times 3 =$ _____   ⑪ $5 \times 7 =$ _____

⑫ $72 \div 8 =$ _____   ⑬ $56 \div 7 =$ _____   ⑭ $54 \div 6 =$ _____

⑮ $3 \times 8 =$ _____   ⑯ $5 \times 4 =$ _____   ⑰ $10 \times 2 =$ _____

⑱ $81 \div 9 =$ _____   ⑲ $40 \div 5 =$ _____   ⑳ $49 \div 7 =$ _____

㉑ $2 \times 3 \times 4 =$ _____   ㉒ $2 \times 4 \times 6 =$ _____

㉓ $1 \times 3 \times 5 =$ _____   ㉔ $0 \times 4 \times 8 =$ _____

㉕ $65 \div 9 =$ _____   ㉖ $40 \div 6 =$ _____

㉗ $25 \div 3 =$ _____   ㉘ $31 \div 4 =$ _____

Do the multiplication and division.

㉙ $6\overline{)48}$

㉚ $5\overline{)35}$

㉛ $7\overline{)28}$

㉜ $2\overline{)18}$

㉝ $4\overline{)32}$

㉞ $3\overline{)18}$

㉟ $8\overline{)56}$

㊱ $9\overline{)36}$

㊲ $\begin{array}{r} 6 \\ \times\ 7 \\ \hline \end{array}$

㊳ $\begin{array}{r} 8 \\ \times\ 2 \\ \hline \end{array}$

㊴ $\begin{array}{r} 1 \\ \times\ 5 \\ \hline \end{array}$

㊵ $\begin{array}{r} 9 \\ \times\ 9 \\ \hline \end{array}$

㊶ $\begin{array}{r} 3 \\ \times\ 9 \\ \hline \end{array}$

㊷ $\begin{array}{r} 4 \\ \times\ 9 \\ \hline \end{array}$

㊸ $\begin{array}{r} 0 \\ \times\ 7 \\ \hline \end{array}$

㊹ $\begin{array}{r} 5 \\ \times\ 6 \\ \hline \end{array}$

㊺ $9\overline{)63}$

㊻ $2\overline{)14}$

㊼ $5\overline{)45}$

㊽ $3\overline{)24}$

㊾ $6\overline{)49}$

㊿ $4\overline{)33}$

(51) $8\overline{)45}$

(52) $7\overline{)56}$

Write the fact families for each group of numbers.

㊣

```
_____ X _____ = _____

_____ X _____ = _____

_____ ÷ _____ = _____

_____ ÷ _____ = _____
```

㊹

```
_____ X _____ = _____

_____ X _____ = _____

_____ ÷ _____ = _____

_____ ÷ _____ = _____
```

Fill in the missing numbers.

㊵ ☐ X 5 = 35

35 ÷ 5 = ☐

㊶ 56 ÷ ☐ = 7

☐ X 7 = 56

㊷ 3 X ☐ = 27

27 ÷ 3 = ☐

㊸ 8 X ☐ = 48

48 ÷ 8 = ☐

㊾ ☐ X 4 = 28

28 ÷ ☐ = 4

㊿ 54 ÷ ☐ = 6

☐ X 6 = 54

㉛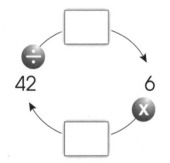

㉜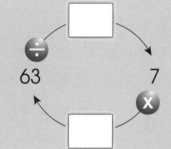

㉝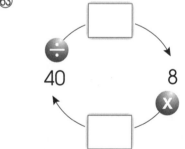

㉞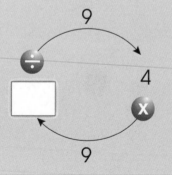

㉟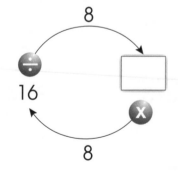

㊱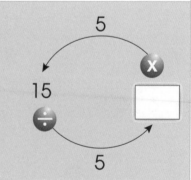

Put the following cards in the right places.

 | 2 | 4 | 5 | 6 | 7 | 32 | x | ÷

⑥⑦ $4 \times \underline{\hspace{1.5cm}} = 16$

⑥⑧ $25 \div \underline{\hspace{1.5cm}} = 5$

⑥⑨ $63 \div 9 = \underline{\hspace{1.5cm}}$

⑦⓪ $9 \times \underline{\hspace{1.5cm}} = 54$

⑦① $8 \underline{\hspace{1.5cm}} 8 = 64$

⑦② $16 \div \underline{\hspace{1.5cm}} = 8$

⑦③ $\underline{\hspace{1.5cm}} \div 5 = 6 \, R \, 2$

⑦④ $31 \underline{\hspace{1.5cm}} 4 = 7 \, R \, 3$

Fill in the blanks.

⑦⑤ $3 \times 4 \times \underline{\hspace{1.5cm}} = 0$

⑦⑥ $2 \times \underline{\hspace{1.5cm}} \times 5 = 10$

⑦⑦ $2 \times 3 \times \underline{\hspace{1.5cm}} = 60$

⑦⑧ $3 \times 3 \times \underline{\hspace{1.5cm}} = 54$

⑦⑨ $4 \times 8 = 8 \times \underline{\hspace{1.5cm}}$
  $= \underline{\hspace{1.5cm}}$

⑧⓪ $4 \times 3 = \underline{\hspace{1.5cm}} \times 6$
  $= \underline{\hspace{1.5cm}}$

⑧① $5 \times 0 = \underline{\hspace{1.5cm}} \times 6$
  $= \underline{\hspace{1.5cm}}$

⑧② $18 \div 3 = \underline{\hspace{1.5cm}} \div 2$
  $= \underline{\hspace{1.5cm}}$

⑧③ $12 \div 3 = 16 \div \underline{\hspace{1.5cm}}$
  $= \underline{\hspace{1.5cm}}$

⑧④ $0 \times 3 = \underline{\hspace{1.5cm}} \div 3$
  $= \underline{\hspace{1.5cm}}$

⑧⑤ $\underline{\hspace{1.5cm}} \div 5 = 12 \div \underline{\hspace{1.5cm}}$
  $= 4$

⑧⑥ $3 \times 3 = 72 \div \underline{\hspace{1.5cm}}$
  $= \underline{\hspace{1.5cm}}$

Write a multiplication sentence and a division sentence for each statement.

ⓐ 48 scouts divided into 6 teams of 8 scouts

_____ X _____ = _____   _____ ÷ _____ = _____

ⓑ 5 sketch books at $7 each, totalling $35

_____ X _____ = _____   _____ ÷ _____ = _____

Solve the problems. Show your work.

ⓐ Dad plants a row of 8 cypress trees on each side of the driveway. How many cypress trees does Dad plant in all?

_____ = _____

Dad plants _____ cypress trees in all.

ⓑ A bag of marbles is shared equally among 9 children. Each child gets 4 marbles. How many marbles are there in the bag?

_____ = _____

There are _____ marbles in the bag.

ⓒ If the marbles in ⓑ are divided equally among 6 children, how many marbles does each child have?

_____ = _____

Each child has _____ marbles.

ⓓ 34 balloons are shared equally among 4 children. How many balloons does each child have? How many balloons are left over?

_____ = _____

Each child has _____ balloons. _____ balloons are left over.

Section III

Overview

In Section II, children practised multiplication and division. They also used fact families to explore the relationship between multiplication and division.

In this section, these skills are built upon to include multiples, factors and mixed operations including brackets. Calculators are used to solve problems beyond the required pencil-and-paper skills.

Children investigate the attributes of 3-D figures such as prisms and pyramids, and 2-D figures such as rhombuses and parallelograms. They are also expected to identify transformations, such as flips, slides and turns. Rotations are limited to quarter turn, half turn and three-quarter turn.

1 Multiples

Multiples - the result of multiplying a number again and again

e.g.

	1	2	3	4	5	6	7	· · · ·
Multiples of 2	2	4	6	8	10	12	14	· · · ·

Column - a list of numbers going up or down

Row - a list of numbers going across

Diagonal - a list of numbers going from one corner to the opposite corner

Nancy has made a 10-column number board. Do what she says.

1	2	3	4	5	6	7	8	9	10
11	12	13	14	15	16	17	18	19	20
21	22	23	24	25	26	27	28	29	30
31	32	33	34	35	36	37	38	39	40
41	42	43	44	45	46	47	48	49	50
51	52	53	54	55	56	57	58	59	60
61	62	63	64	65	66	67	68	69	70
71	72	73	74	75	76	77	78	79	80
81	82	83	84	85	86	87	88	89	90
91	92	93	94	95	96	97	89	99	100

2 times table

$2 \times 1 = 2$
$2 \times 2 = 4$
Multiples of 2

5 times table

$5 \times 1 = 5$
$5 \times 2 = 10$
Multiples of 5

10 times table

$10 \times 1 = 10$
$10 \times 2 = 20$
Multiples of 10

4 times table

$4 \times 1 = 4$
$4 \times 2 = 8$
$4 \times 3 = 12$
$4 \times 4 = 16$
$4 \times 5 = 20$
Multiples of 4

8 times table

$8 \times 1 = 8$
$8 \times 2 = 16$
$8 \times 3 = 24$
$8 \times 4 = 32$
$8 \times 5 = 40$
Multiples of 8

① Put a ╱ over every multiple of 2.

② Put a ╲ over every multiple of 4.

③ Circle the multiples of 5.

④ Colour the multiples of 10 yellow.

⑤ Colour the multiples of 8 orange.

Look at Nancy's board again. Fill in the blanks.

⑥  Multiples of 4 are also multiples of _____ .

⑦  Multiples of 8 are also multiples of _____ and _____ .

⑧  How do the multiples of 5 run, in rows, columns or diagonally ?

_____

⑨  How do the multiples of 8 run?

_____

⑩ Which numbers are multiples of 8 and 10?

_____

⑪  Are the multiples of 2, 4, 8 and 10 even or odd numbers?

_____

Look what Nancy marked on her board. Fill in the blanks.

1	2	3	4	5	6	7	8	9	10
11	12	13	14	15	16	17	18	19	20
21	22	23	24	25	26	27	28	29	30
31	32	33	34	35	36	37	38	39	40
41	42	43	44	45	46	47	48	49	50
51	52	53	54	55	56	57	58	59	60
61	62	63	64	65	66	67	68	69	70
71	72	73	74	75	76	77	78	79	80
81	82	83	84	85	86	87	88	89	90
91	92	93	94	95	96	97	98	99	100

⑫ All the numbers marked with ▢ are the multiples of _____ .

⑬ All the numbers marked with ▢ are the multiples of _____ and _____ .

⑭ All the numbers marked with ◉ are the multiples of _____ .

⑮ Which numbers are multiples of 3 and 11? _____

⑯ Which number is a multiple of 3, 9 and 11? _____

⑰ Are the multiples of 9 also the multiples of 3? _____

⑱ How do the multiples of 3, 9 and 11 run? _____

Look at Nancy's 7-column number board. Then do the questions.

1	2	3	4	5	6	7
8	9	10	11	12	13	14
15	16	17	18	19	20	21
22	23	24	25	26	27	28
29	30	31	32	33	34	35
36	37	38	39	40	41	42
43	44	45	46	47	48	49
50	51	52	53	54	55	56
57	58	59	60	61	62	63
64	65	66	67	68	69	70

⑲ Cross X the multiples of 7.

⑳ Circle the multiples of 6.

㉑ How do the multiples of 7 run?

_____

㉒ How do the multiples of 6 run?

_____

㉓ _____ is a multiple of 6 and 7.

㉔ From 1 to 70, there are _____ multiples of 7.

Write the numbers.

㉕ Write the first five multiples of 8. _____

㉖ Write the first five multiples of 6. _____

㉗ Write the multiples of 9 between 25 and 53. _____

㉘ Write the multiples of 7 between 34 and 52. _____

㉙ Write the multiples of 11 between 52 and 86. _____

㉚ Write the multiples of 6 between 74 and 93. _____

㉛ Write the multiples of 8 between 68 and 91. _____

Tick ✔ the right statements.

Multiples of Even Numbers	
2	2, 4, 6, 8, 10, 12, ...
4	4, 8, 12, 16, 20, 24, ...

Multiples of Odd Numbers	
3	3, 6, 9, 12, 15, 18, ...
5	5, 10, 15, 20, 25, 30, ...

Multiples of 3

3	6	9	12
3 + 0	6 + 0	9 + 0	1 + 2

15	18	21	....
1 + 5	1 + 8	2 + 1	

Multiples of 9

9	18	27	36
9 + 0	1 + 8	2 + 7	3 + 6

45	54	63	....
4 + 5	5 + 4	6 + 3	

㉜ Even numbers only have even multiples. ☐

㉝ Odd numbers do not have even multiples. ☐

㉞ Odd numbers alternate even and odd multiples. ☐

㉟ The digits of the multiples of 3 add to 3, 6, 9, 12 ..... . ☐

㊱ All multiples of 3 end with 3, 6 or 9. ☐

㊲ The multiples of 9 are even numbers. ☐

㊳ The digits of the multiples of 9 add to 9, 18, 27, 36 ..... . ☐

ACTIVITY

Help Nancy count how much she has to pay for the food.

1.

No.	1	2	3	4	5	6
$	2	4				

They are the multiples of ☐ .

2.

No.	1	2	3	4	5	6
$	7	14				

They are the multiples of ☐ .

2 Brackets

Brackets - signs used in pairs for showing us which part to do first
( )

e.g. $5 - (1 + 2) = 5 - 3$ ←——— First, solve the problem
$= 2$ inside the ( ).

Read what Nancy says and fill in the blanks.

①

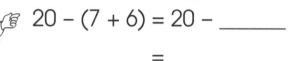
Three of us have 20 🌻 in all. Jill has 7 🌻 and Lily has 6 🌻. How many 🌻 do I have?

Do the problem inside the brackets first.

$20 - (7 + 6) = 20 -$ _____

$=$ _____

Nancy has _____ 🌻.

②

I have 15 🍬. Lily gives me 6 🍬. Jill has 13 🍬. Lily gives her 5 🍬. How many more 🍬 do I have than Jill?

$(15 + 6) - (13 + 5) =$ _____ $-$ _____

$=$ _____

Nancy has _____ more 🍬 than Jill.

Try these.

③ $(11 + 6) - 4$
$=$ _____ $-$ _____
$=$ _____

④ $(25 + 49) + 15$
$=$ _____ $+$ _____
$=$ _____

⑤ $(58 - 23) - 16$
$=$ _____ $-$ _____
$=$ _____

⑥ $52 - (4 + 29)$
$=$ _____ $-$ _____
$=$ _____

⑦ $16 + (92 - 68)$
$=$ _____ $+$ _____
$=$ _____

⑧ $14 + (41 - 27)$
$=$ _____ $+$ _____
$=$ _____

⑨ $(25 + 16) - 21 = $ _____

⑩ $32 - (16 + 9) = $ _____

⑪ $5 + (13 + 28) - 40 = $ _____

⑫ $70 - (25 + 8) - 16 = $ _____

Write the numbers.

⑬

I picked 4 🌼, then 2 🌼, then 6 🌼.

$4 + 2 + 6 = $ _____

⑭

I picked 6 🌼, then 2 🌼, then 4 🌼.

$6 + 2 + 4 = $ _____

Even if the order of addition changes, the answer is still the same.

⑮ $4 + 2 + 6 = $ _____ $+ 2 + 4 = $ _____ $+ 4 + 6 = $ _____

Try these.

⑯ $3 + 9 + 7$

$= (3 + 7) + 9$

$= $ _____ $+$ _____

$= $ _____

⑰ $16 + 23 + 4$

$= (16 + $ _____ $) + $ _____

$= $ _____ $+$ _____

$= $ _____

Quick Addition
If 2 numbers make 10, 20, 30, ..., add them first.

⑱ $29 + 7 + 1$

$= (29 + $ _____ $) + 7$

$= $ _____

⑲ $15 + 26 + 5$

$= (15 + $ _____ $) + 26$

$= $ _____

 𝒜𝒞𝒯ℐ𝒱ℐ𝒯𝒴

Find the answer.

Start with the inside and work it out!

$20 - (10 + (12 - (4 + 2)))$

$= 20 - (10 + (12 - $ _____ $)) = $ _____

3 Addition and Subtraction

WORDS TO LEARN

Estimate - guess how many or how much

Read what Nancy says. Then help her find the size of the audience in the dancing show.

> Estimate by rounding the number to the nearest thousand.

①

	Show A	Estimate
Week 1	2416	2000
Week 2	1270	1000
Week 3	+ 2738	+ 3000
Total		

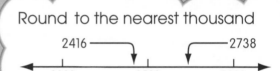

Round to the nearest thousand

2416 ⟶   ⟵ 2738

2000   2500   3000

2416, being closer to 2000 than 3000, rounds to 2000.

2738, being closer to 3000 than 2000, rounds to 3000.

2500, being halfway between 2000 and 3000, rounds to 3000.

A number halfway between two numbers rounds to the larger number.

②

	Show B	Estimate
Week 1	2789	
Week 2	1968	
Week 3	+ 1237	+
Total		

Try these without estimating.

③
```
   1623
   2496
+   776
_____
```

④
```
   4135
     26
+   469
_____
```

⑤
```
   1257
     89
+ 2519
_____
```

⑥
```
   2507
   2930
+   604
_____
```

⑦ 379 + 1258 + 7147 = _____

⑧ 5098 + 61 + 436 = _____

⑨ 737 + 6940 + 259 = _____

⑩ 373 + 8499 + 59 = _____

Do the estimates. Then find the number of children attending the dancing show.

⑪

	Show A	Estimate
Total	6 4 2 4	6 0 0 0
Adult	– 2 3 2 5	– 2 0 0 0
Children		

Round the numbers to the nearest thousand to do estimation.

⑫

	Show B	Estimate
Total	5 9 9 4	
Adult	– 2 0 7 6	–
Children		

If you can't take away, borrow 10 from the column before.

Try these without estimating.

⑬ 5260 – 1449 = _____   ⑭ 3768 – 2509 = _____

⑮ 4736 – 2559 = _____   ⑯ 1258 – 979 = _____

⑰ 6137 – 4988 = _____   ⑱ 3525 – 2069 = _____

ACTIVITY

Do these sums. Then colour the answers below to help Nancy find her dancing shoes.

1. 4703 – 3613
2. 2502 – 147
3. 498 + 165 + 2064
4. 1735 + 1046 + 99
5. 7600 – 2669
6. 4765 – 949
7. 6509 + 144 + 783
8. 2130 – 1498

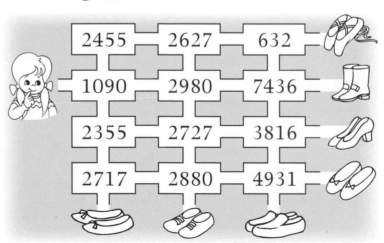

2455	2627	632
1090	2980	7436
2355	2727	3816
2717	2880	4931

Multiplication

4

WORDS TO LEARN

Multiplication - a short way to find a sum when the addends are the same

e.g. $5 + 5 + 5 = 3 \times 5 = 15$

Multiplicand Multiplier Product

Solve the problems. Then write the letters in the boxes to find what Nancy says.

① a	② n	③ f	④ r	⑤ i	⑥ n	⑦ a
3	7	6	10	6	9	8
x 7	x 5	x 4	x 8	x 3	x 3	x 8

⑧ t	⑨ t	⑩ e	⑪ u	⑫ c	⑬ o	⑭ s
7	9	10	8	8	3	9
x 6	x 8	x 3	x 4	x 5	x 2	x 6

⑮

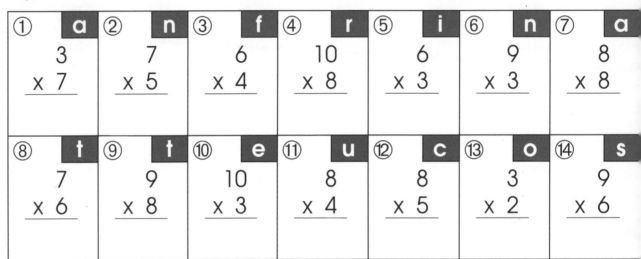

Y	6	32			21	80	30
24	64	27	42	21	54	72	18	40	!

Read what Nancy says. Then fill in the blanks.

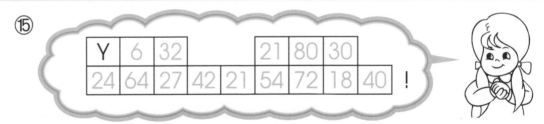

1st Multiply the ones digit.
2nd Multiply the tens digit.

$$\begin{array}{r} 1\,2 \\ \times\ \ 4 \\ \hline 8 \end{array} \Rightarrow \begin{array}{r} 1\,2 \\ \times\ \ 4 \\ \hline 4\,8 \end{array} \Rightarrow \begin{array}{r} 1\,2 \\ \times\ \ 4 \\ \hline 4\,8 \end{array}$$

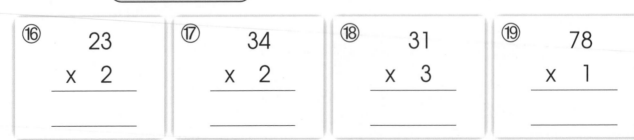

⑯	⑰	⑱	⑲
23	34	31	78
x 2	x 2	x 3	x 1

⑳	㉑	㉒	㉓
43 x 3	52 x 3	84 x 2	73 x 3

Help Nancy count how much she has to pay. Write the numbers.

㉔

 1 costs 26¢. How much do 3 cost?

26 x 3 = _____

3 cost _____¢

$$\begin{array}{r} \overset{1}{2}6 \\ \times\ \ 3 \\ \hline 8 \end{array} \Rightarrow \begin{array}{r} \overset{1}{2}6 \\ \times\ \ 3 \\ \hline 7\,8 \end{array}$$

> **1st** Multiply the ones digit.
> 6 x 3 = 18, which is 1
> ten and 8 ones. Carry
> 1 to the tens.
>
> **2nd** Multiply the tens digit.
> 2 tens x 3 = 6 tens
> Add the 1 ten from
> step 1, making 7 tens
> in all.

㉕

1 costs 27¢. How much do 4 cost?

27 x _____ = _____

4 cost _____¢

$$\begin{array}{r} 2\,7 \\ \times\ \underline{} \\ \underline{} \end{array}$$

Estimate first. Then do the problems.

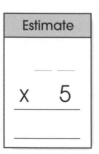

> Round the numbers
> to the nearest ten;
> then estimate.

㉖	Estimate
19 x 5	2 0 x 5

㉗	Estimate
2 8 x 7	___ x 7

㉘	Estimate
3 9 x 6	___ x 6

㉙	Estimate
4 8 x 7	___ x 7

㉚	Estimate
5 3 x 5	___ x 5

Read what Nancy says. Then help her write the numbers.

㉛ There are 126 cookies in a box. How many cookies are there in 6 boxes?

| Hundreds column |
| Tens column |
| Ones column |

H T O

```
  1 2 6
x     6
-------
    3 6  ← (6 x 6 = 36)
  1 2 0  ← (20 x 6 = 120)
+ 6 0 0  ← (100 x 6 = 600)
-------
  7 5 6
```

1st Multiply the ones digit.

Carry 3 tens to tens.

```
      3
  1 2 6
x     6
-------
    [ ]
```

2nd Multiply the tens digit.

Carry 1 hundred to hundreds.

```
  1 3
  1 2 6
x     6
-------
  [ ] 6
```

3rd Multiply the hundreds digit.

```
  1 3
  1 2 6
x     6
-------
  [ ] 5 6
```

There are _____ cookies in 6 boxes.

㉜  A box of biscuits weighs 225 g. What is the weight of 7 boxes?

225 x 7 = _____

The weight of 7 boxes of biscuits is _____ grams.

```
  2 2 5
x     7
-------
```

Estimate first. Then do the problems.

㉝
```
  3 9 2
x     3
-------
```

Estimate
``   4 0 0
x   3
-------```

㉞
```
  4 0 6
x     9
-------
```

Estimate
`` x   9
-------```

Round the numbers to the nearest hundred; then estimate.

㉟
```
  3 0 5
x     8
-------
```

Estimate
`` x   8
-------```

㊱
```
  5 4 5
x     3
-------
```

Estimate
`` x   3
-------```

㊲
```
  6 1 4
x     4
-------
```

Estimate
`` x   4
-------```

Help Nancy solve the problems.

㊳	How many 🍬 are there in 7 cans? _346_ x __7__ = _____ There are _____ 🍬 in 7 cans.	$\begin{array}{r} 3\,4\,6 \\ \times \quad 7 \\ \hline \end{array}$
㊴ 	How many 🍭 are there in 5 boxes? _____ x _____ = _____ There are _____ 🍭 in 5 boxes.	$\begin{array}{r} \\ \times \quad \\ \hline \end{array}$
㊵ 	How many 🍬 are there in 8 boxes? _____ x _____ = _____ There are _____ 🍬 in 8 boxes.	$\begin{array}{r} \\ \times \quad \\ \hline \end{array}$
㊶ 	How many 🍴 are there in 4 boxes? _____ x _____ = _____ There are _____ 🍴 in 4 boxes.	$\begin{array}{r} \\ \times \quad \\ \hline \end{array}$

 # ACTIVITY

Use a calculator to find the products. Circle Yes or No.

1. 7 x 4 x 6 = ☐   2. 52 x 9 x 11 = ☐

   6 x 4 x 7 = ☐   9 x 52 x 11 = ☐

   4 x 6 x 7 = ☐   11 x 52 x 9 = ☐

3. Does changing the order of multiplication change the product?   Yes   No

5 Division

Divisible - can be divided with no remainder

Remainder - what is left over when you divide

e.g.

$$14 \div 3 = 4\ r\ 2$$

dividend   divisor   quotient   remainder

e.g.

$$6 \div 3 = 2 \quad \text{(6 is divisible by 3)}$$

divisor ⌐ quotient

$$\begin{array}{r} 4\ r\ 2 \leftarrow \text{remainder} \\ 3\overline{)14} \leftarrow \text{dividend} \\ \underline{12} \\ 2 \leftarrow \text{remainder} \end{array}$$

Complete the table.

	Dividend	Divisor	Equation
	26	4	26 ÷ 4 = 6 r 2
①			67 ÷ 8 = r
②			43 ÷ 7 = r
③	32	9	÷ = r
④	58	6	÷ = r

Find the problems with remainder 1 and write the letters to finish what Nancy says.

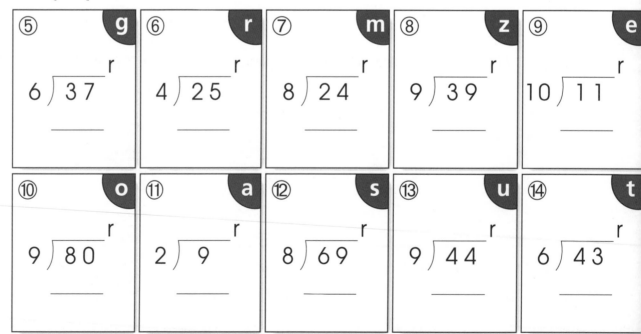

⑤ **g** 6)‾3 7   r ____

⑥ **r** 4)‾2 5   r ____

⑦ **m** 8)‾2 4   r ____

⑧ **z** 9)‾3 9   r ____

⑨ **e** 10)‾1 1   r ____

⑩ **o** 9)‾8 0   r ____

⑪ **a** 2)‾9   r ____

⑫ **s** 8)‾6 9   r ____

⑬ **u** 9)‾4 4   r ____

⑭ **t** 6)‾4 3   r ____

⑮

You are ___ ___ ___ ___ ___ !

How does Nancy divide the cookies? Write the numbers.

⑯ Divide 63 cookies into 3 groups; each group has _____ cookies.

⑰ Divide 46 cookies into 4 groups; each group has _____ cookies. There are _____ left over.

Read what Nancy says. Then write the numbers.

Share 26 cookies between 2 people.

$26 \div 2 = 13$

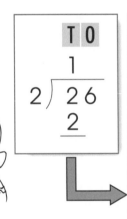

```
   T O
    1
2 ) 2 6
    2
```

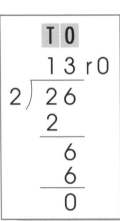

```
   T O
   1 3  r 0
2 ) 2 6
    2
    6
    6
    0
```

4 steps to do division:
1st	2nd
Divide	Multiply
3rd	4th
Subtract	Bring down

⑱
```
        r
4 ) 8 4
___

___
```

⑲
```
        r
5 ) 5 7
___

___
```

⑳
```
        r
3 ) 9 9
___

___
```

㉑
```
        r
6 ) 6 8
___

___
```

㉒ $59 \div 5 =$ _____ r _____

㉓ $69 \div 2 =$ _____ r _____

㉔ $79 \div 7 =$ _____ r _____

㉕ $64 \div 3 =$ _____ r _____

㉖ $86 \div 4 =$ _____ r _____

㉗ $89 \div 8 =$ _____ r _____

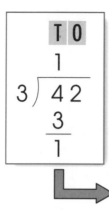

Share 42 cookies among 3 people.

$42 \div 3 = 14$

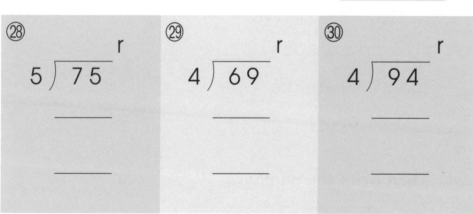

T	O
	1

$3 \overline{)\ 4\ 2}$
$\quad\ 3$
$\quad\ \overline{\ 1}$

T	O
	1 4 r 0

$3 \overline{)\ 4\ 2}$
$\quad\ 3$
$\quad\ \overline{1\ 2}$
$\quad\ 1\ 2$
$\quad\ \overline{\quad\ 0}$

4 steps to do division:
1st Divide
2nd Multiply
3rd Subtract
4th Bring Down

㉘
$5 \overline{)\ 7\ 5}$ r ___

___

㉙
$4 \overline{)\ 6\ 9}$ r ___

___

㉚
$4 \overline{)\ 9\ 4}$ r ___

___

㉛ $53 \div 4 =$ _____ r _____

㉜ $83 \div 3 =$ _____ r _____

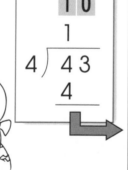

Share 43 cookies among 4 people.

$43 \div 4 = 10\ r\ 3$

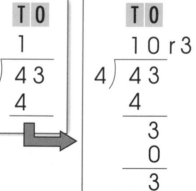

T	O
	1

$4 \overline{)\ 4\ 3}$
$\quad\ 4$

T	O
	1 0 r 3

$4 \overline{)\ 4\ 3}$
$\quad\ 4$
$\quad\ \overline{\ 3}$
$\quad\ \ 0$
$\quad\ \overline{\ 3}$

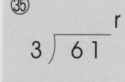

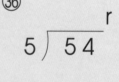

When the dividend is smaller than the divisor, put 0 in the quotient.

㉝
$6 \overline{)\ 6\ 3}$ r ___

___

㉞
$4 \overline{)\ 8\ 2}$ r ___

___

㉟
$3 \overline{)\ 6\ 1}$ r ___

___

㊱
$5 \overline{)\ 5\ 4}$ r ___

___

㊲ $72 \div 7 =$ _____ r _____

㊳ $41 \div 2 =$ _____ r _____

Cross out ✗ Nancy's mistakes and write the correct answers.

㊱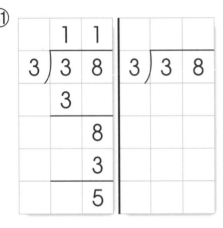

㊵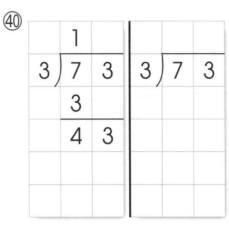

Multiply the divisor by a number to get a product closest to the dividend.

㊶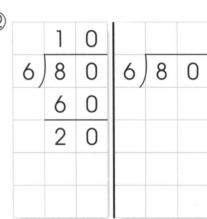

㊷

Oops! I made some mistakes.

A C T I V I T Y

Follow the maze so that the cookie can get to the jar.
It can only go through doors divisible by 4.

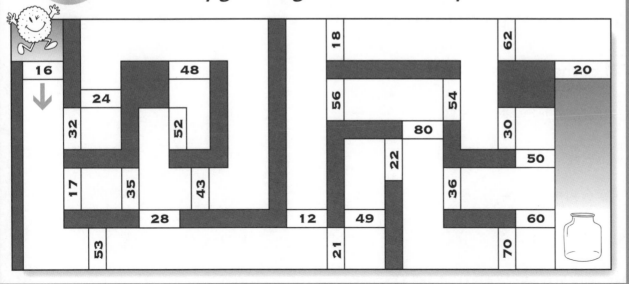

⑥ Length

Kilometre (km) - a unit for measuring distance between places
e.g. distance between towns

Millimetre (mm) - a unit for measuring a short length
e.g. measuring rainfall

1 km = 1000 m
1 m = 100 cm
1 cm = 10 mm

Look at Nancy's picture map. Find the distances.

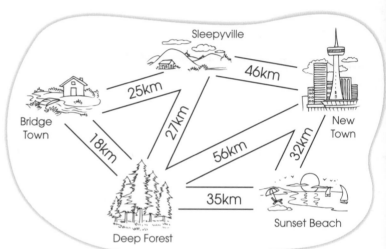

① From Bridge Town to
   Deep Forest: _____ km

② From Sleepyville to
   New Town: _____ km

③ From Deep Forest to
   Sunset Beach: _____ km

Find the shortest distances.

④ From Bridge Town to Sunset Beach = _____ km + _____ km = _____ km

⑤ From Sleepyville to Sunset Beach = _____ km + _____ km = _____ km

⑥ From Bridge Town to New Town = _____ km + _____ km = _____ km

Fill in the blanks.

⑦ 2000 m + 4 m = _____ m

⑧ 3400 m − 3 km = _____ m

⑨ 6 km + 8 m = _____ m

⑩ 2400 m + 1600 m = _____ km

⑪ 400 m + 200 m + 400 m = _____ km

km $\xrightarrow{\times 1000}$ m
   $\xleftarrow{\div 1000}$

e.g.
2.2km = 2.2 x 1000m
      = 2200m
2400m = 2400 ÷ 1000km
      = 2.4km

Find and write the amount of rain water Nancy collected last week.

⑫

SUN	MON	TUE	WED	THU	FRI	SAT	10mm = 1cm

10mm = 1cm

1cm

We say 15mm, not 1cm5mm.

_____mm _____mm _____mm _____mm _____mm _____mm _____mm

⑬ The total amount of rain on Monday and Thursday was _____ mm.

⑭ The total amount of rain on Tuesday and Friday was _____ mm.

⑮ There was _____ mm more rain on Tuesday than on Saturday.

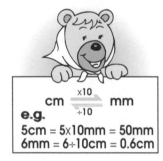

cm $\xrightarrow{\times 10}$ mm
$\xleftarrow{\div 10}$

e.g.
5cm = 5×10mm = 50mm
6mm = 6÷10cm = 0.6cm

Fill in the blanks.

⑯ 9 cm = _____ mm

⑰ 3 cm + 4 mm = _____ mm

⑱ 5 cm + 8 mm = _____ mm

⑲ 6 cm – 17 mm = _____ mm

⑳ 8 cm – 6 mm = _____ mm

㉑ 32 cm – 30 cm = _____ mm

A C T I V I T Y

Answer the questions.

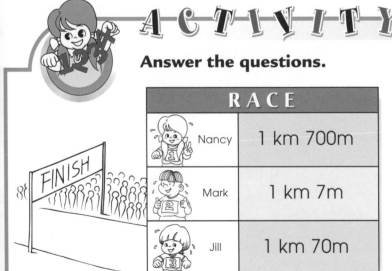

RACE	
Nancy	1 km 700m
Mark	1 km 7m
Jill	1 km 70m

1. Who ran the farthest?
   _____

2. How much farther did Jill run than Mark?
   _____m

3. How far did Nancy run?
   _____m

7 Time

Second - a unit for measuring time

1 hour	= 60 minutes
1 minute	= 60 seconds

Arrange the TV programmes in order from 1 to 7. Then write the times.

My favourite programmes.

①

Sunday Special

	9:00 a.m.	Cartoon Time	
	11:50 a.m.	Music Video	
1	8:25 a.m.	Uncle Sam's Time	25 minutes past 8
	8:55 p.m.	Toy Street	
	4:45 p.m.	Games for Kids	
	10:15 a.m.	Movie Time	
	7:20 p.m.	Top Ten Songs	

Look at ① again. Write the answers or draw the clock hands.

② Toy Street ends at 9:55 p.m. This programme lasts _____ minutes.

③ Top Ten Songs ends at 8:15 p.m. This programme lasts _____ minutes.

④ Music Video lasts 30 minutes.

It ends at _____ .

⑤ Games for Kids lasts 35 minutes.

It ends at _____ .

Read what Nancy says. Then write the times.

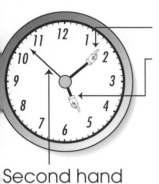

Minute hand

Hour hand

Second hand

The second hand completes one revolution in 60 seconds. We use second to measure short periods of time.

Hour   Minute   Second

The time shown on a digital clock is like this:

05:07:52

⑥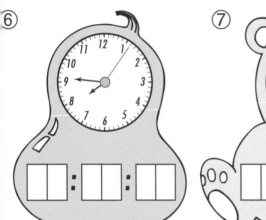

⑦

⑧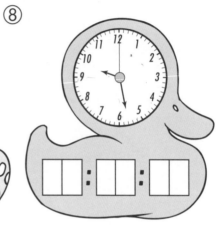

Fill in the blanks with hours, minutes or seconds.

⑨ I walk to school in 10 _____ .

⑩ I spend about 7 _____ in school every day.

⑪ In the 100-metre race, I was faster than Jill by 3 _____ .

ACTIVITY

Nancy timed her friends in the race. Answer the questions.

GEORGE
0:09:34

FELIX
0:09:11

PETER
0:11:13

1. Who was the fastest?

_____

2. Who was the slowest?

_____

8 Triangles

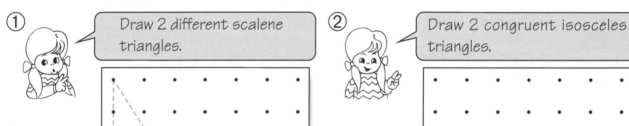

Venn diagram - a diagram of overlapping circles to show what things have in common

Triangle - any shape with 3 sides

e.g. right triangle - a triangle with a right angle

equilateral triangle - a triangle with 3 sides equal

isosceles triangle - a triangle with 2 sides equal

scalene triangle - a triangle with no equal sides

Congruent - having the same size and shape

Draw what Nancy says.

① Draw 2 different scalene triangles.

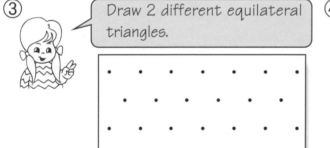

② Draw 2 congruent isosceles triangles.

③ Draw 2 different equilateral triangles.

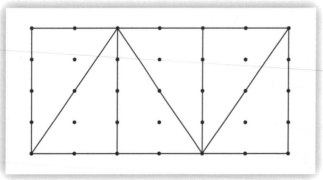

④ Draw the biggest right and isosceles triangle.

Help Nancy count the triangles in this figure.

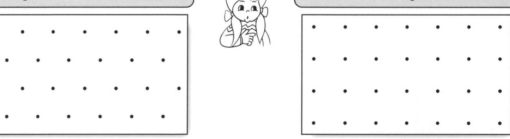

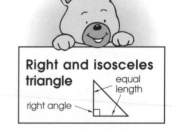

Right and isosceles triangle — equal length — right angle

⑤ _____ right triangles.

⑥ _____ isosceles triangles.

Read what Jill says. Write the letters in the Venn diagram.

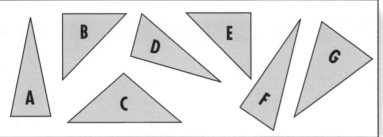

A Venn diagram shows what 2 groups have in common.
e.g.

Nancy likes ice cream and candy. Lily likes chips and candy. Both like candy.

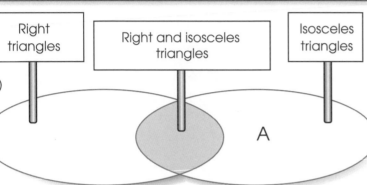

Right triangles

Right and isosceles triangles

Isosceles triangles

⑦

A

Read what Lily says. Then draw lines.

⑧
Draw 3 lines to make 4 right triangles.

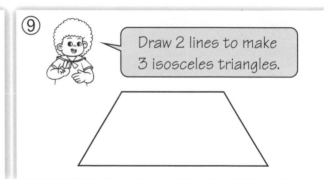

⑨
Draw 2 lines to make 3 isosceles triangles.

ACTIVITY

Do the questions.

1. Draw a line on each square to continue the tile pattern.

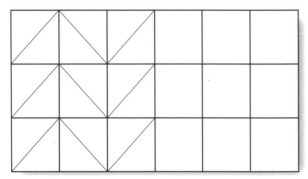

2. In each group, colour the congruent figures.

Perimeter

Perimeter - the distance around the outside of a shape

Help Nancy write the perimeters of her waist and her wrist.

① 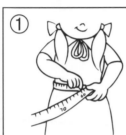 Nancy's waist is

about _____ cm.

② 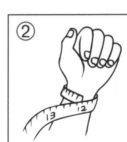 Nancy's wrist is

about _____ cm.

Find the perimeters of the shapes by counting squares.

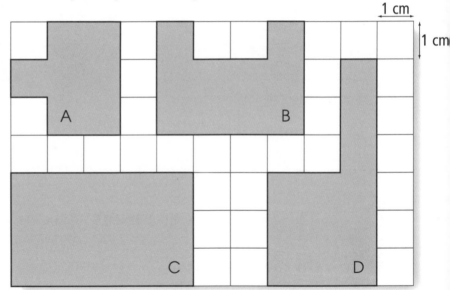

1 cm

1 cm

	Shape	Perimeter
③	A	cm
④	B	cm
⑤	C	cm
⑥	D	cm

Find the perimeters.

⑦ 12m

3m

Perimeter

= 12 m + 3 m + 12 m + 3 m

= _____ m

⑧ 10m

10m

Perimeter

= 10 m + ____ m + ____ m + ____ m

= _____ m

⑨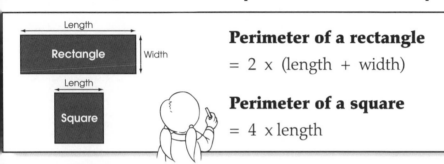

Perimeter

$= 7$ cm $+$ _____ cm $+$ _____ cm $+$ _____ cm

$=$ _____ cm

⑩

Perimeter

$=$ _____ cm $+$ _____ cm $+$ _____ cm $+$ _____ cm

$=$ _____ cm

Use the formulas to find the perimeters of the shapes.

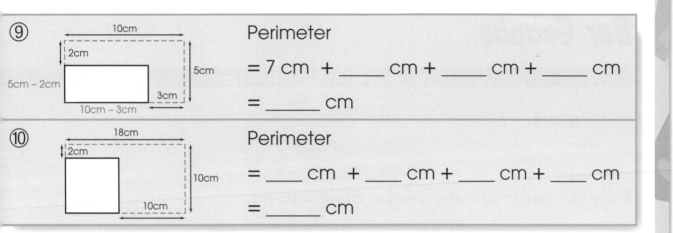

Perimeter of a rectangle

$= 2$ x (length $+$ width)

Perimeter of a square

$= 4$ x length

Do the problem inside the brackets first.

⑪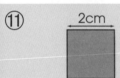
2cm

Perimeter $= 4$ X _____ cm

$=$ _____ cm

⑫
4cm
2cm

Perimeter $= 2$ X (_____ cm $+$ _____ cm)

$=$ _____ cm

ACTIVITY

All of these shapes have 8 squares.
Colour the shape with the longest perimeter.

1cm

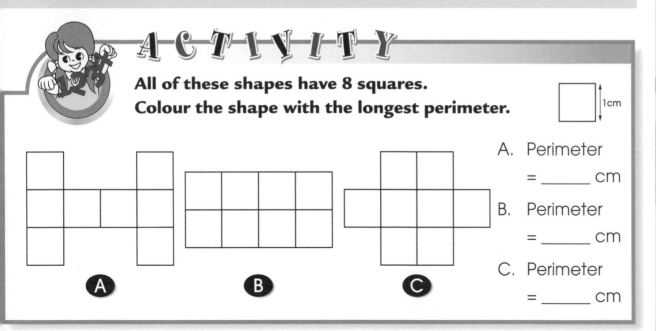

A   B   C

A. Perimeter

$=$ _____ cm

B. Perimeter

$=$ _____ cm

C. Perimeter

$=$ _____ cm

Bar Graphs

Bar graph - a graph made up of rectangular bars

Tally - a method to record the numbers in groups of 5 ||||

Read the bar graph and answer the questions.

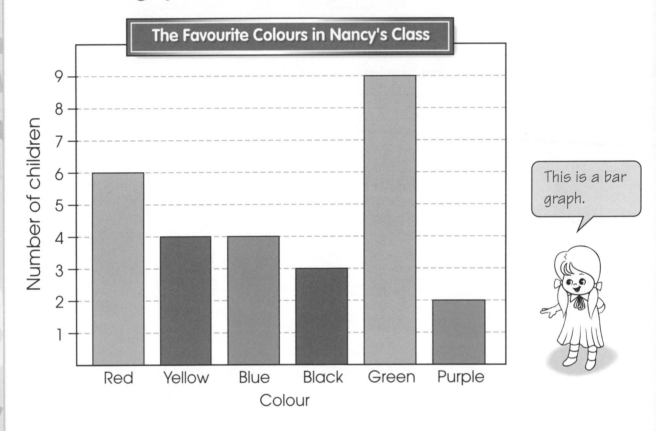

The Favourite Colours in Nancy's Class

This is a bar graph.

① Which is the most popular colour? _____

② Which is the next most popular colour? _____

③ Which is the least popular colour? _____

④ Which colour is only liked by 3 children? _____

⑤ How many children like red and green? _____

⑥ How many more children like green than purple? _____

⑦ Which 2 colours are liked by the same number of children? _____

⑧ How many children are there in all? _____

Read the table and colour the boxes to complete the graph. Then answer the questions.

Toast	＋＋＋ ||
Muffin	|||
Cereal	＋＋＋ ＋＋＋
Waffle	＋＋＋ |||

This is what my classmates have for breakfast.

⑨

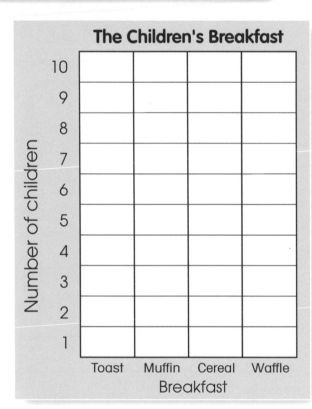

The Children's Breakfast

Number of children

10
9
8
7
6
5
4
3
2
1

Toast   Muffin   Cereal   Waffle
Breakfast

⑩ How many children prefer toast? _____

⑪ Which food is the least popular for breakfast?

_____

⑫ Which food is liked by 8 children? _____

⑬ How many children are in Nancy's class? _____

𝔸ℂ𝕋𝕀𝕍𝕀𝕋𝕐

Use the clues to draw the shapes.

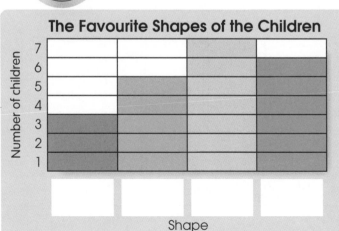

The Favourite Shapes of the Children

Number of children

7
6
5
4
3
2
1

Shape

1. Seven children like ◯.

2. Fewest children like ▢.

3. 1 more child likes ◯ than △.

4. 2 more children like ◇ than ▢.

5-digit Numbers

WORDS TO LEARN

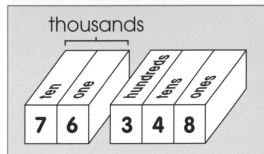

thousands

ten	one	hundreds	tens	ones
7	6	3	4	8

Standard form : 76 348

Expanded form : 70 000 + 6 000 + 300 + 40 + 8

Words : Seventy-six thousand three hundred forty-eight

How many people live in these towns? Fill in the blanks.

①  Floraton
Population
12 360

Expanded form:

10 000 +   +   +   + 0
_____

Words:
          thousand   hundred
_____

②  Brighton
Population
56 334

Expanded form:
_____

Words:
_____

Write the numbers.

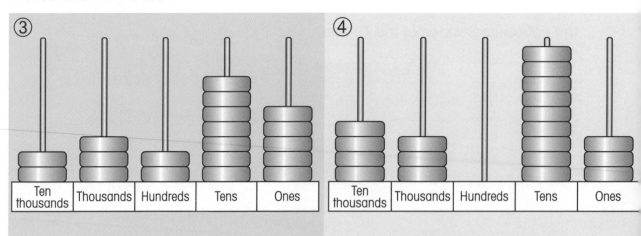

③

Ten thousands	Thousands	Hundreds	Tens	Ones

_____

④

Ten thousands	Thousands	Hundreds	Tens	Ones

_____

⑤ Write the largest 5-digit number. _____

⑥ Write the smallest 5-digit odd number. _____

⑦ Write the next five numbers after 79 997.

_____

⑧ Put these numbers in order from smallest to largest.

25 063   26 053   20 653   20 563   23 056

_____

> Separate hundreds and thousands with a space or ",".
> e.g. 76 348 or 76,348

Write the place value of the underlined digits.

⑨ 6<u>3</u> 042 _____

⑩ 58 4<u>6</u>9 _____

⑪ <u>4</u>7 264 _____

⑫ 39 <u>2</u>48 _____

 **Complete the number patterns.**

		58000	68000			98000
	148000				87000	
238000	248000		268000		86000	
	448000		64000		84000	94000

Fill in the blanks. (4 marks)

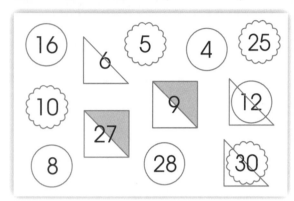

① ◯ are multiples of 2 and _____ .

② ◺ are multiples of _____ .

③ ✿ are multiples of _____ .

④ ◣ are multiples of 3 and _____ .

Write the numbers. (4 marks)

⑤ Write the first three multiples of 6. _____

⑥ Write the multiples of 8 between 46 and 57. _____

⑦ Write the multiples of 11 between 71 and 95. _____

⑧ Write the multiples of 7 between 53 and 65. _____

Write the numbers. (26 marks)

⑨
$$12 - (8 + 2)$$
$$= 12 - \underline{}$$
$$= \underline{}$$

⑩
$$(19 - 2) + 16$$
$$= \underline{} + 16$$
$$= \underline{}$$

⑪
$$89 - (17 + 43)$$
$$= \underline{} - \underline{}$$
$$= \underline{}$$

⑫
$$56 - (27 - 9)$$
$$= \underline{} - \underline{}$$
$$= \underline{}$$

⑬
$$(40 - 13) + (15 + 7)$$
$$= \underline{} + \underline{}$$
$$= \underline{}$$

⑭
```
  1 6 2 5
  1 4 0 9
+ 3 2 8 8
_____
```

⑮
```
  3 7 5 4
    9 7 7
+ 2 6 5 9
_____
```

⑯
```
  2 0 4 7
    9 3 2
+ 5 9 2 4
_____
```

⑰
```
   3777
 - 2909
 _____

 _____
```

⑱
```
   6530
 - 4816
 _____

 _____
```

⑲
```
   3200
 - 1499
 _____

 _____
```

⑳ There are 6257 children. 2392 of them are boys.
How many of them are girls? _____

㉑ Emily has 1388 beads. Jane has 2066 beads.
How many do they have in all? _____

Find the answers. (24 marks)

㉒
```
    37
 x   9
 _____

 _____
```

㉓
```
    89
 x   7
 _____

 _____
```

㉔
```
   489
 x   6
 _____

 _____
```

㉕
```
   569
 x   2
 _____

 _____
```

㉖
```
        r
 6 ) 85
```

㉗
```
        r
 6 ) 77
```

㉘
```
        r
 5 ) 65
```

㉙
```
        r
 3 ) 97
```

㉚
```
        r
 4 ) 82
```

㉛
```
   450
 x   7
 _____

 _____
```

㉜
```
        r
 5 ) 96
```

㉝
```
   108
 x   5
 _____

 _____
```

Look at the picture and find the shortest distances. (6 marks)

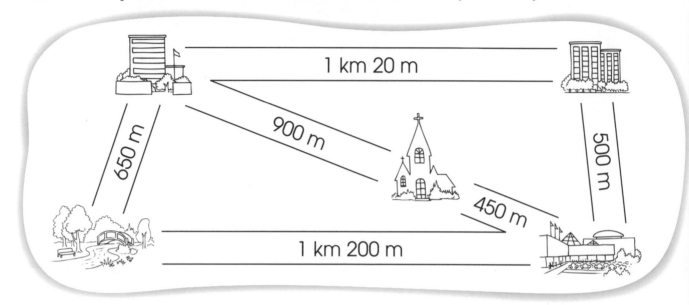

34 From 🌉 to 🏢 = _____ m

35 From 🏢 to 🏢 = _____ m

36 From 🌉 to 🏛 = _____ m

37 From 🏢 to 🏛 = _____ m + _____ m = _____ m

38 From ⛪ to 🌉 = _____ m + _____ m = _____ m

39 From ⛪ to 🏢 = _____ m + _____ m = _____ m

Write the times. (3 marks)

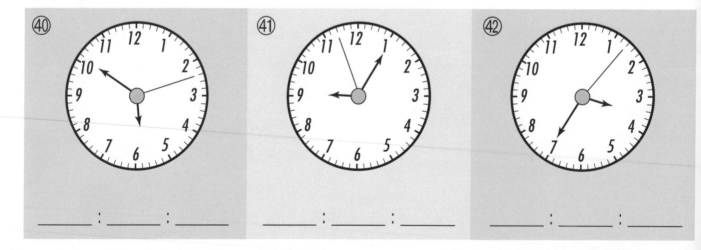

40 _____ : _____ : _____

41 _____ : _____ : _____

42 _____ : _____ : _____

Draw the clock hands. (4 marks)

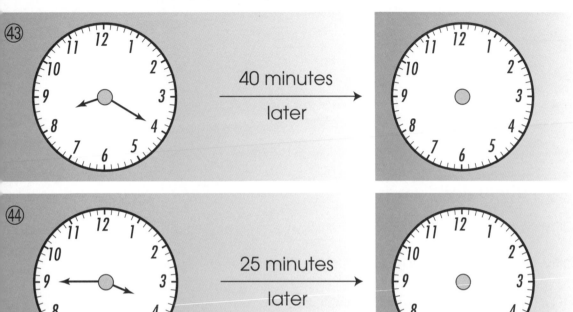

㊸

40 minutes
later

㊹

25 minutes
later

Find the perimeters of the shaded squares or rectangles. (8 marks)

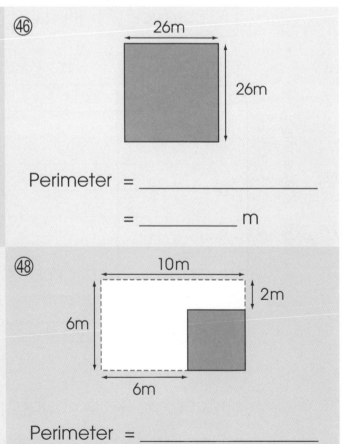

㊺
48cm

39cm

Perimeter = _____

= _____ cm

㊻
26m

26m

Perimeter = _____

= _____ m

㊼
16cm

3cm

8cm

10cm

Perimeter = _____

= _____ cm

㊽
10m

2m

6m

6m

Perimeter = _____

= _____ m

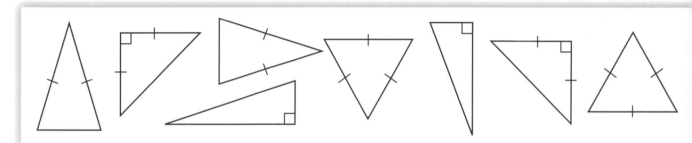

Fill in the blanks. (4 marks)

49 How many right triangles? _____

50 How many isosceles triangles? _____

51 How many equilateral triangles? _____

52 How many right and isosceles triangles? _____

Colour the boxes to complete the bar graph and answer the questions. (7 marks

| Basketball | ‖‖‖ ‖ |
| Baseball | ‖‖‖ ‖‖‖ |

| Soccer | ‖‖‖ |
| Hockey | ‖‖‖ |

53 **The Favourite Sports**

Number of students

9
8
7
6
5
4
3
2
1

Basketball   Baseball   Soccer   Hockey

Sport

54 How many children like basketball most? _____

55 How many fewer children like hockey than baseball? _____

56 How many children are there in all? _____

Read the bar graph and answer the questions. (4 marks)

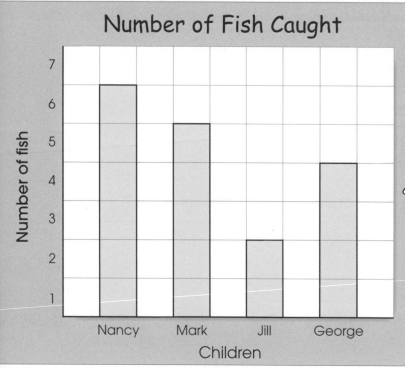

Number of Fish Caught

57. Who caught the most fish? _____

58. How many fish did Jill catch? _____

59. How many more fish did Mark catch than George? _____

60. How many fish did the children catch in all? _____

Write the place value of the underlined digits. (4 marks)

61. 46 793 _____

62. 52 479 _____

63. 37 246 _____

64. 10 054 _____

Write in words. (2 marks)

65. 20 654 _____

66. 37 049 _____

SCORE

100

Factors

WORDS TO LEARN

Factors - the numbers that are multiplied to get a product

e.g.

$$6 \times 3 = 18$$

factors   product   3 and 6 are factors of 18.

Read what Nancy says. Then fill in the blanks.

①   I can put 6  into 2 different rectangular boxes.

a. 6 = 3 x _____

b. 6 = 1 x _____

Factors of 6 are:

1 , 2 , 3 , 6

②   I can put 12 into 3 different rectangular boxes.

a. 12 = 3 x _____

b. 12 = 2 x _____

d. Factors of 12 are:

_____ , _____ , _____ ,

_____ , _____ , _____

c. 12 = 1 x _____

③   I can put 20 into 3 different rectangular boxes.

a. 20 = 2 x _____

b. 20 = 4 x _____

d. Factors of 20 are:

_____ , _____ , _____ ,

_____ , _____ , _____

c. 20 = 1 x _____

Colour the rectangles with 20 blocks yellow, those with 32 blocks green and those with 36 blocks red.

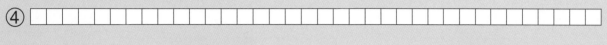
④

⑤   ⑥    ⑦ 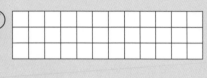   ⑧

⑩

⑨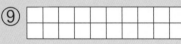

⑪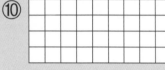

⑬

⑫   ⑭

Look at the above rectangles. Complete the following.

⑮   20 = 1 x 20 = _____ x _____ = _____ x _____

⑯   32 = 1 x 32 = _____ x _____ = _____ x _____

⑰   36 = 1 x 36 = _____ x _____ = _____ x _____ = _____ x _____ = _____ x _____

⑱   The factors of 20 : _____

⑲   The factors of 32 : _____

⑳   The factors of 36 : _____

Find the numbers which have the factors of 1 and themselves only. Colour them red.

㉑

| 11 | 12 | 13 | 14 | 15 | 16 | 17 | 18 | 19 | 20 |

Find the factors of these numbers.

㉒ 18 = __1__ x _____

   = _____ x _____

   = _____ x _____

   The factors of 18 :

   _____

㉓ 28 = _____ x _____

   = _____ x _____

   = _____ x _____

   The factors of 28 :

   _____

You can use the multiplication facts to find the factors of a number.

㉔ The factors of 15 : _____

㉕ The factors of 22 : _____

㉖ The factors of 30 : _____

㉗ The factors of 42 : _____

Help Nancy find all the different ways to divide her cup cakes equally.

 has 28 .

㉘

28		group(s)		number of in each group
28	÷	1	=	28
28	÷	2	=	☐
28	÷	3	=	✕
28	÷	4	=	☐
28	÷	5	=	✕
28	÷	6	=	✕
28	÷	7	=	4

(28 cannot be divided equally by 3, 5 or 6)

repeated, STOP!

The factor of a number can divide into the number without remainder.

Stop dividing when a factor you have got shows up again.

㉙ The factors of 28 : _____

㉚ 24 ÷ 1 = ☐

24 ÷ 2 = ☐

24 ÷ 3 = ☐

24 ÷ 4 = ☐

24 ÷ 5 = ☒

24 ÷ 6 = ☐ (repeated)

The factors of 24 :

_____

㉛ 30 ÷ 1 = ☐

30 ÷ 2 = ☐

30 ÷ 3 = ☐

30 ÷ 4 = ☒

30 ÷ 5 = ☐

30 ÷ 6 = ☐ (repeated)

The factors of 30 :

_____

Use division to find the factors of these numbers.

㉜ 8   The factors of 8   : _____

㉝ 35   The factors of 35   : _____

㉞ 48   The factors of 48   : _____

㉟ 60   The factors of 60   : _____

ACTIVITY

Read what the children say. Then help them write the numbers on their cards.

1. This number is
    • between 15 and 20
    • a factor of 32

2. This number is
    • between 44 and 50
    • a factor of 96

3. This number is
    • between 13 and 20
    • a factor of 84

13 More about Division

Remainder - what is left over when you divide

e.g.

$$346 \div 3 = 115 \text{ r } 1$$

dividend   divisior   quotient   remainder

Help Nancy's uncle find how many and were sold each day.

① 248 were sold in 2 days.

1st → $2\overline{)248}$ Divide the hundreds.

2nd → $2\overline{)248}$ Divide the tens.   2 | Bring down   Subtract 0   4

3rd → $2\overline{)248}$ Divide the ones.   2 | Bring down   4   4 ↓   Subtract 0   8

$248 \div 2 = $ _____

Nancy's uncle sold _____ each day.

② 363 were sold in 3 days.

$363 \div 3 = $ _____

$3\overline{)363}$

Nancy's uncle sold _____ each day.

_____

_____

Try these.

③ $844 \div 4 = $ _____

④ $639 \div 3 = $ _____

⑤ $864 \div 2 = $ _____

⑥ $558 \div 5 = $ _____

⑦ $337 \div 3 = $ _____

⑧ $689 \div 2 = $ _____

⑨ $489 \div 4 = $ _____

⑩ $668 \div 6 = $ _____

Read what Nancy's uncle says and do the questions.

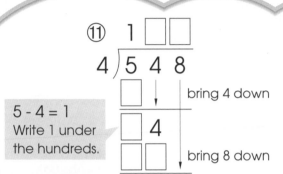

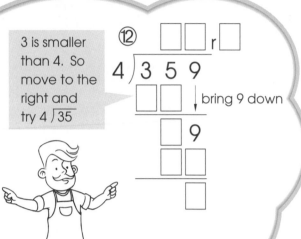

⑬
$$5\overline{)627}$$

⑭
$$3\overline{)263}$$

⑮
$$4\overline{)527}$$

⑯
$$6\overline{)599}$$

⑰
$$5\overline{)456}$$

⑱
$$3\overline{)467}$$

⑲
$$7\overline{)856}$$

⑳
$$9\overline{)842}$$

㉑ $653 \div 7 =$

㉒ $322 \div 5 =$

㉓ $768 \div 9 =$

㉔ $546 \div 8 =$

Read what Nancy and her uncle say. Then do the division.

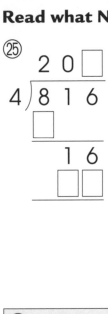

㉕

```
   2 0 □
4 ) 8 1 6
    □
    ─────
      1 6
    □ □
    ─────
```

When the dividend is smaller than the divisor, write "0" in the quotient and bring the whole number down to the next column.

When we divide 0, the answer is 0.

㉖

```
      8 □
5 ) 4 0 0
    □ □
    ─────
        0
        □
    ─────
```

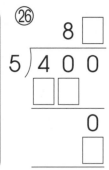

If you divide 0 by any number, the answer is always 0.
e.g. **0 ÷ 5 = 0**

㉗ $5\overline{)405}$	㉘ $5\overline{)409}$	㉙ $7\overline{)749}$	㉚ $4\overline{)508}$
㉛ $3\overline{)618}$	㉜ $2\overline{)290}$	㉝ $5\overline{)520}$	㉞ $2\overline{)260}$
㉟ $9\overline{)954}$	㊱ $8\overline{)880}$	㊲ $6\overline{)720}$	㊳ $7\overline{)709}$

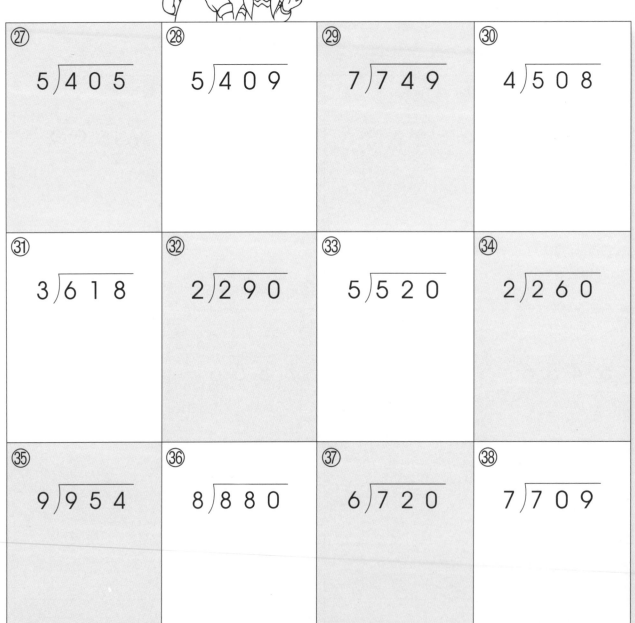

Solve the problems.

③⑨ Emily put 148 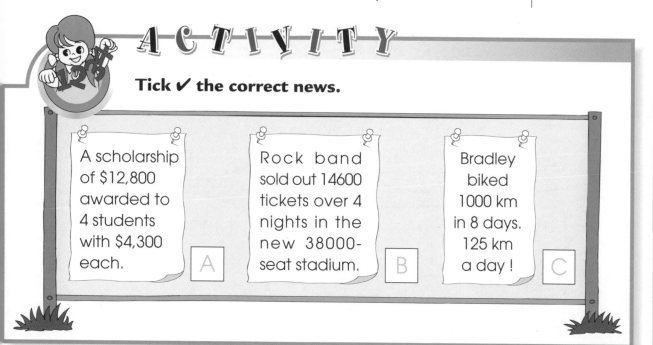 in 4 boxes. How many were there in each box?

_____ ÷ _____ = _____

There were _____ in each box.

④⓪ Nancy put 108 in 9 boxes. How many were there in each box?

_____ ÷ _____ = _____

There were _____ in each box.

④① Nancy's uncle earned $468 in 6 days. How much did he earn each day?

_____ ÷ _____ = _____

He earned $ _____ each day.

④② There were 328 customers in 8 days. How many customers were there each day?

_____ ÷ _____ = _____

There were _____ customers each day.

ACTIVITY

Tick ✔ the correct news.

A scholarship of $12,800 awarded to 4 students with $4,300 each. ☐ A

Rock band sold out 14600 tickets over 4 nights in the new 38000-seat stadium. ☐ B

Bradley biked 1000 km in 8 days. 125 km a day ! ☐ C

Mixed Operations

WORDS TO LEARN

X - multiplication sign	÷ - division sign
+ - addition sign	— - subtraction sign

Read what Nancy says. Help her find how many treats she and her friends got on Halloween.

① 4 houses each gave me 2 and the next house gave me 1 . How many treats did I get? $4 \times 2 + 1 = $ _____ $+ 1 = $ _____

I got _____ treats.

1st
Divide or multiply.
2nd
Add or subtract.

② 6 of my friends shared 24 and my mom gave each of them 1 more. How many treats did each get?

$24 \div 6 + 1 = $ _____ $+ 1 = $ _____

Each got _____ .

The treats with answer 72 belong to Nancy. Colour them yellow.

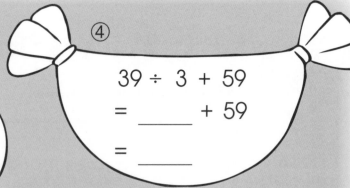

③ $56 \times 2 - 36$
= _____ $- 36$
= _____

④ $39 \div 3 + 59$
= _____ $+ 59$
= _____

⑤ $194 - 61 \times 2$
= _____ $-$ _____
= _____

⑥ $144 - 135 \div 3$
= _____ $-$ _____
= _____

Find the number of treats that Nancy and her sisters got.

⑦ I have 2 sisters. Each of them got 12 treats. They shared the treats with me. How many treats did each of us get?

12 x 2 ÷ 3 = _____ ÷ 3 = _____

Each of us got _____ treats.

For multiplication and division, do the one that comes first.

The children could get treats from the houses with even numbers. Do the questions and find the houses. Colour them yellow.

⑧ 10 ÷ 2 x 5
= ____ x 5
= ____

⑨ 41 x 4 ÷ 2
= ____ ÷ 2
= ____

⑩ 156 ÷ 4 x 3
= ____ X ____
= ____

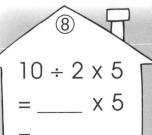

⑪ 53 x 9 ÷ 3
= ____ ÷ ____
= ____

⑫ 243 ÷ 9 x 6
= ____ X ____
= ____

⑬ 369 ÷ 3 x 4
= ____ X ____
= ____

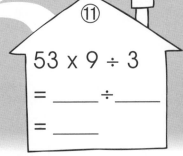

ACTIVITY

Read what Nancy says. Then colour her costume yellow.

I shared $42 with my 2 sisters. Then I used the money to buy costume. I had $8 left.

A.  $5

B.  $8

C.  $6

D.  $4

Money

$ - dollar sign   ¢ - cent sign

e.g.   78¢ = $ 0.78

$ 0.78

dollars   cents

Nancy is playing cashier. Write the values of the bills in the boxes.

① $ [ ]   5

② $ [ ]   10

③ $ [ ]   50

④ $ [ ]   20

⑤ $ [ ]   100

Help Nancy circle enough bills or coins to trade her uncle's bills.

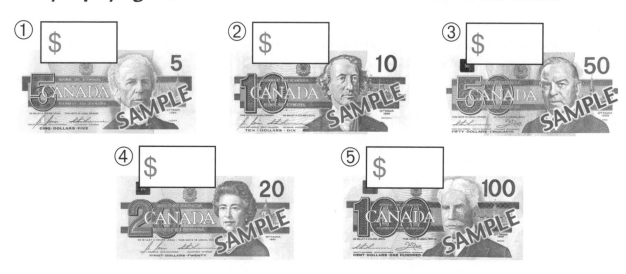

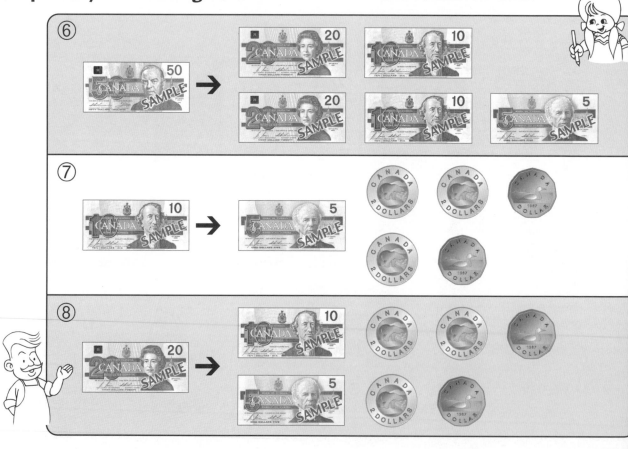

Read what Nancy says. Then fill in the chart.

$0.56 means
0 dollars and 56 cents.
$ 0.56 = 56 ¢

dollars | cents
$ 0.50

	Coins	Cents	Dollars
⑨		¢	$ 0.
⑩		¢	$
⑪		¢	$

Help Nancy fill in the chart and count how much each person has paid.

⑫	$10	$5	25¢	1¢
Number of bills or coins	2	1	2	1
Total	$ 20	$	¢	¢

⑬ Total amount = $

⑭	$10	$5	25¢	5¢
Number of bills or coins				
Total	$	$	¢	¢

⑮ Total amount = $

Help Nancy give the change.

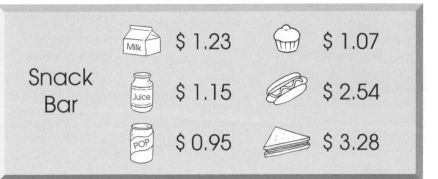

Snack Bar

Milk	$ 1.23	cupcake	$ 1.07
Juice	$ 1.15	hot dog	$ 2.54
POP	$ 0.95	sandwich	$ 3.28

Align the decimal points to do addition or subtraction.

Purchase	Total	Money given	Change

⑯

Total:
$ 1.23
+ $ 2.54
$ ___ . ___

Money given:

Change:
```
    5  9 10
$ 6. 0 0
- $ 3. 7 7
```
$ ___ . ___

⑰

Total:
$ 0.95
+ $ ___ . ___
$ ___ . ___

Money given:

Change:
$ 5.00
- $ ___ . ___
$ ___ . ___

⑱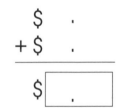

Total:
$ ___ . ___
+ $ ___ . ___
$ ___ . ___

Money given: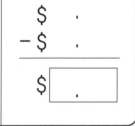

Change:
$ ___ . ___
- $ ___ . ___
$ ___ . ___

⑲

Total:
$ ___ . ___
$ ___ . ___
+ $ ___ . ___
$ ___ . ___

Money given:

Change:
$ ___ . ___
- $ ___ . ___
$ ___ . ___

ill has $7.00. Help her find the total cost of each group of things. Then colour the groups of things she can buy.

⑳

Total = $ [.   ]

㉑

Total = $ [.   ]

㉒

Total = $ [.   ]

㉓
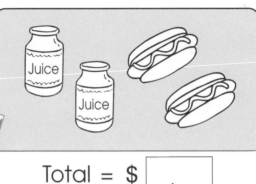
Total = $ [.   ]

ACTIVITY

Circle the bills to answer each riddle.

1. I have 4 bills worth $40.

2. I have 4 bills worth $75.

3. I have 5 bills worth $100.

Fractions

WORDS TO LEARN

Fraction - a number showing a part of a whole

e.g.  one third of the circle is shaded. $\frac{1}{3}$ is shaded. $\frac{1}{3}$ — numerator — denominator

Colour the fraction of the apples that Nancy picked.

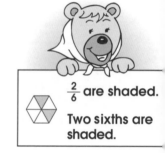
$\frac{2}{6}$ are shaded.
Two sixths are shaded.

① $\frac{3}{10}$

② $\frac{7}{10}$

③ $\frac{4}{9}$ ④ $\frac{5}{7}$

Nancy's mom made some apple pies. How much did each child eat? Write the fractions.

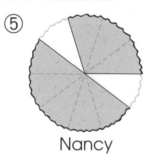
⑤ $\frac{2}{10}$
Nancy

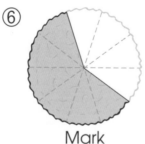
⑥
Mark

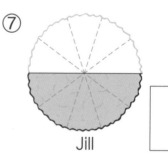
⑦
Jill

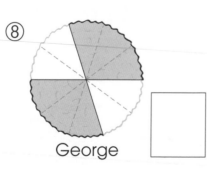
⑧
George

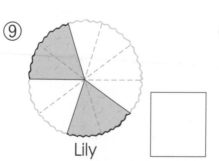
⑨
Lily

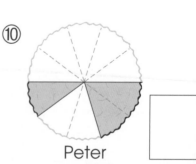
⑩
Peter

Read what Nancy says. Then write the numbers.

⑪ How many  are there in $\frac{2}{3}$ of 6 ?

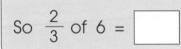 Divide 6 equally into 3 groups.

Take 2 groups. 2 groups have 4 .

$\frac{2}{3}$ means

2 out of every 3.

So $\frac{2}{3}$ of 6 = ☐

⑫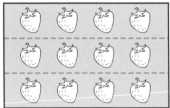

$\frac{1}{3}$ of 12 = ☐

⑬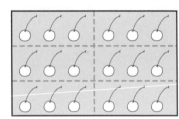

$\frac{2}{6}$ of 18 = ☐

⑭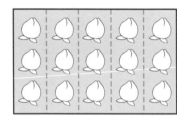

$\frac{1}{5}$ of 15 = ☐

⑮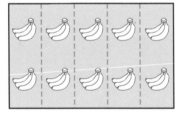

$\frac{3}{5}$ of 10 = ☐

⑯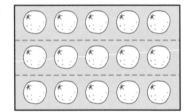

$\frac{2}{3}$ of 15 = ☐

⑰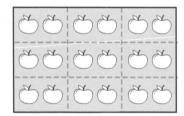

$\frac{1}{9}$ of 18 = ☐

Tick ✔ the right boxes to match what Nancy's mother says.

⑱ Check the oven every $\frac{1}{4}$ hour.   A☐   B☐   C☐

⑲ Add $\frac{1}{2}$ teaspoon of sugar to the mix.   A☐   B☐   C☐

⑳ Add $\frac{1}{3}$ of the glass of water. A☐   B☐   C☐

See how the children cut their pies. Then find how much they ate altogether.

㉑

Altogether they ate

$$\frac{1}{8} + \frac{1}{8} = \boxed{\frac{}{8}}$$

㉒

Altogether they ate

$$\frac{1}{6} + \boxed{\frac{}{}} = \boxed{\frac{}{}}$$

㉓

Altogether they ate

$$\boxed{\frac{}{}} + \boxed{\frac{}{}} = \boxed{\frac{}{}} = 1$$

Try these.

㉔ $\dfrac{2}{7} + \dfrac{3}{7} = \underline{\quad}$

㉕ $\dfrac{6}{10} + \dfrac{2}{10} = \underline{\quad}$

$\bigoplus = \bigcirc$

$\dfrac{4}{4} = 1$

When the denominators are the same, add the numerators only.

㉖ $\dfrac{1}{5} + \dfrac{2}{5} = \underline{\quad}$

㉗ $\dfrac{5}{8} + \dfrac{2}{8} = \underline{\quad}$

㉘ $\dfrac{4}{6} + \dfrac{1}{6} = \underline{\quad}$

㉙ $\dfrac{1}{7} + \dfrac{6}{7} = \dfrac{}{7} = \underline{\quad}$

㉚ $\dfrac{1}{10} + \dfrac{8}{10} = \underline{\quad}$

㉛ $\dfrac{4}{9} + \dfrac{5}{9} = \dfrac{}{9} = \underline{\quad}$

Find the leftovers. Write the fractions.

㉜ 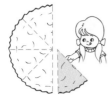 $\dfrac{5}{8} - \dfrac{1}{8} = \dfrac{\boxed{}}{\boxed{8}}$

㉝

㉞ 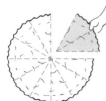 $\dfrac{11}{12} - \dfrac{\boxed{}}{\boxed{12}} = \dfrac{\boxed{}}{\boxed{}}$

$\dfrac{7}{8} - \dfrac{\boxed{}}{\boxed{}} = \dfrac{\boxed{}}{\boxed{}}$

Try these.

㉟ $\dfrac{4}{7} - \dfrac{2}{7} = \underline{\qquad}$

㊱ $\dfrac{7}{9} - \dfrac{4}{9} = \underline{\qquad}$

㊲ $\dfrac{10}{11} - \dfrac{3}{11} = \underline{\qquad}$

㊳ $\dfrac{13}{15} - \dfrac{12}{15} = \underline{\qquad}$

When the denominators are the same, subtract the numerators only.

㊴ $\dfrac{12}{14} - \dfrac{6}{14} = \underline{\qquad}$

㊵ $\dfrac{10}{16} - \dfrac{7}{16} = \underline{\qquad}$

ACTIVITY

Read what Nancy says. Then complete the fractions.

 $\frac{1}{2}$ shaded

 $\frac{2}{4}$ shaded

$$\dfrac{1}{2} = \dfrac{2}{4}$$

$\frac{1}{2}$ and $\frac{2}{4}$ are equivalent fractions.

1.

$\dfrac{1}{2} = \dfrac{\boxed{}}{8}$

2.

$\dfrac{1}{3} = \dfrac{\boxed{}}{6}$

Capacity

WORDS TO LEARN

Capacity - the amount of water that a container can hold

Nancy measured the capacity of the containers with a cup. Read her record. Then answer the questions.

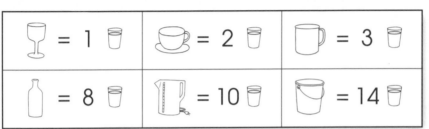

① Tick ✓ the container that holds the most.

A   B   C   D

② Tick ✓ the container that holds the least.

A   B   C   D

③ Put the containers from the least to the most capacity. Arrange them from A to F.

  A    □ 🍾

Which capacity seems reasonable? Tick ✓ the right boxes.

④
- [ ] 1 litre
- [ ] 10 litres
- [ ] 100 litres

⑤
- [ ] 1 litre
- [ ] 10 litres
- [ ] 100 litres

Litre is a unit for measuring capacity. Its symbol is L.

The capacity of a 10cm cube is 1 litre.

⑥
- [ ] 1 litre
- [ ] 10 litres
- [ ] 100 litres

- [ ] 1 litre
- [ ] 10 litres
- [ ] 100 litres

Draw the water level in each container.

⑦  2 L

⑧  3 L

⑨ 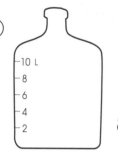 8 L

Nancy pours some water into an empty bucket. How much water is in the bucket?

⑩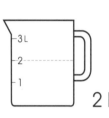

Water in
= 2L – 1L
= ___ L

⑪

Water in
= ___ L – ___ L
= ___ L

⑫

Water in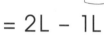
= ___ L – ___ L
= ___ L

 ACTIVITY

Answer the questions.

 2 L   4 L

 10 L   8 L

1. How many of water can be poured into a ?   ☐

2. How many times more water can a  hold than a  ?   ☐ times

Shapes

WORDS TO LEARN

Tile pattern	-	shapes that can cover an area without gaps or overlaps
Line of symmetry	-	a line that divides a shape into 2 matching parts

e.g. ← Line of symmetry

Look at Nancy's drawings. Colour the ones with a tile pattern.

①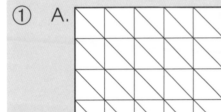

A.   B.   C.

Finish the patterns.

②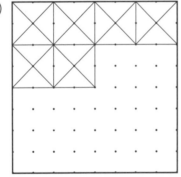

③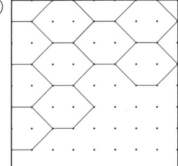

④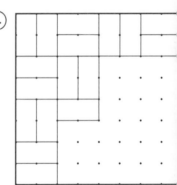

Tick ✔ the shapes that fit together by themselves.

⑤

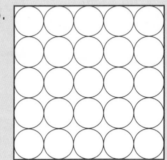

A   B   C

D   E   F

Sort Nancy's pictures. Write the letters in the right boxes.

⑥ No lines of symmetry

⑦ One line of symmetry

⑧ Two lines of symmetry

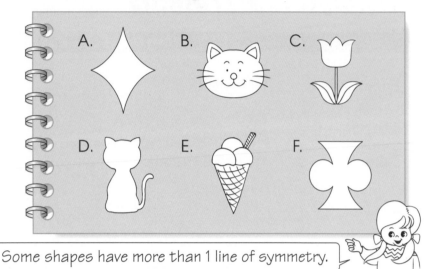

Some shapes have more than 1 line of symmetry.

Draw from the line of symmetry to complete each shape.

⑨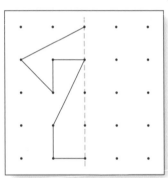

⑩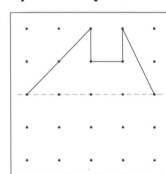

⑪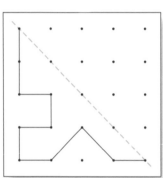

How many lines of symmetry are there? Write the numbers.

⑫

⑬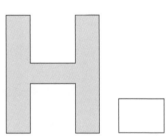

⑭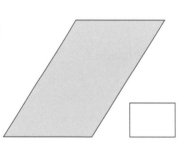

𝔸ℂ𝕋𝕀𝕍𝕀𝕋𝕐

Try to make your own animal tiles.

Cut along the dotted lines.

Stick it there.

Draw an eye and a mouth.

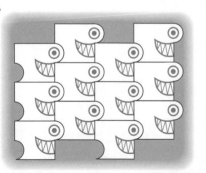

Prisms and Pyramids

WORDS TO LEARN

Face — a flat surface of a solid

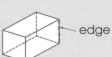

A rectangular prism has 6 faces.

Edge — a curve or a straight line segment where two surfaces or faces meet

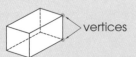

Vertex — a corner of a plane or solid shape

Prism — a solid shape with rectangular faces and congruent ends, named by the shape of its ends

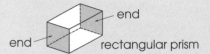

rectangular prism / triangular prism

Pyramid — a solid shape with triangular faces, a common vertex and a flat base, named by the shape of its base

rectangular pyramid / hexagonal pyramid

Cylinder — a solid shape with two circular ends of the same size

circular ends

Which of the mail boxes is each letter for? Draw ◎, ☼, ☺ or ☆.

① Triangular prism ☐ ② Rectangular prism ☐

③ Hexagonal prism ☐ ④ Pentagonal prism ☐

Prisms and pyramids are named by the shape of the ends or bases.

Nancy made some frames with straws and plasticine. Match the bases with the frames. Write the letters and name the frames.

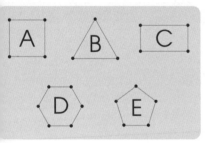

⑤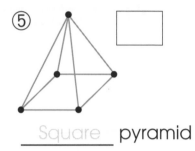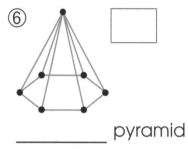

Square pyramid _____ pyramid

⑦ 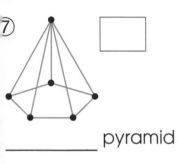 ⑧ 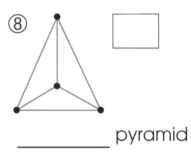 ⑨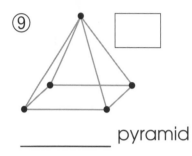

_____ pyramid _____ pyramid _____ pyramid

Write the number of faces and edges of each solid.

⑩ 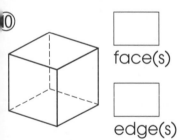 face(s)
edge(s)

⑪  face(s)
edge(s)

⑫ 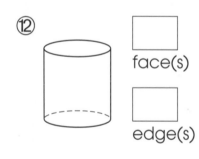 face(s)
edge(s)

ACTIVITY

See how Nancy makes a shape. Then match the nets with the shapes.

Fold it up.

A triangular prism.

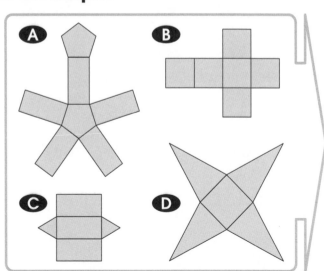

Ⓐ Ⓑ Ⓒ Ⓓ

1.
2.
3.
4.

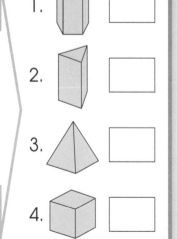

20 Bar Graphs and Circle Graphs

Bar graph   -   a graph using bars to show information

Circle graph -   a graph using parts of a circle to show information about a whole

Read the graph and answer the questions.

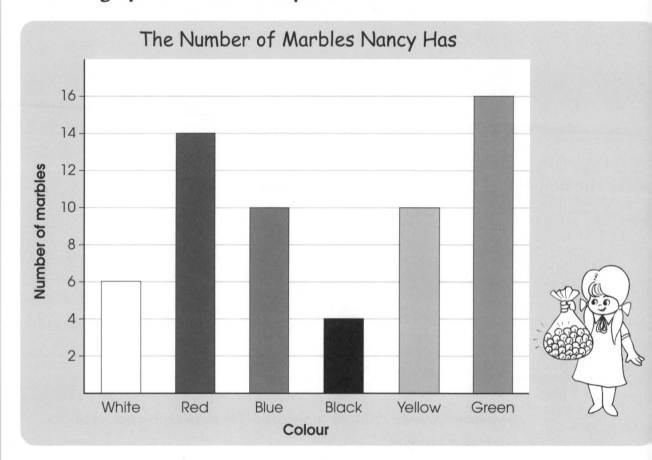

The Number of Marbles Nancy Has

① How many red marbles are there? _____

② How many more green marbles than white marbles are there? _____

③ How many blue and yellow marbles are there? _____

④ Which colour marbles does Nancy have the most? _____

⑤ How many marbles are there in all? _____

Colour the boxes to complete the bar graph and fill in the blanks.

	Nancy	Mark	Jill	George	Lily	Peter
No. of marbles	60	40	50	20	30	60

⑥

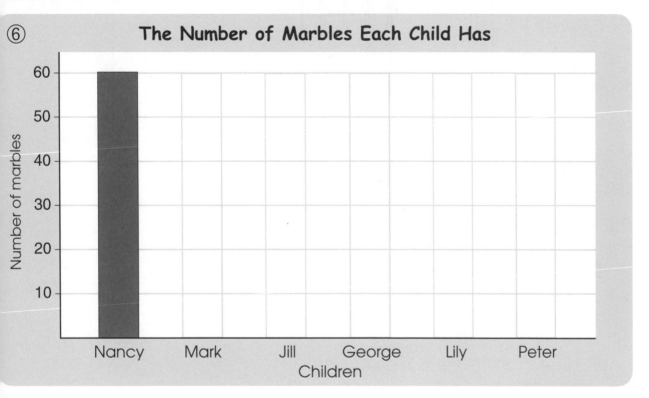

The Number of Marbles Each Child Has

⑦ Nancy has as many marbles as _____ .

⑧ _____ children have more than 45 marbles.

⑨ _____ has the fewest marbles.

⑩ Lily has more marbles than _____ . She has _____ more.

⑪ Mark and Jill have _____ marbles in all.

⑫ Lily and George have _____ marbles in all.

⑬ The children have _____ marbles in all.

Read the newspaper to see what sports the people like. Then fill in the blanks.

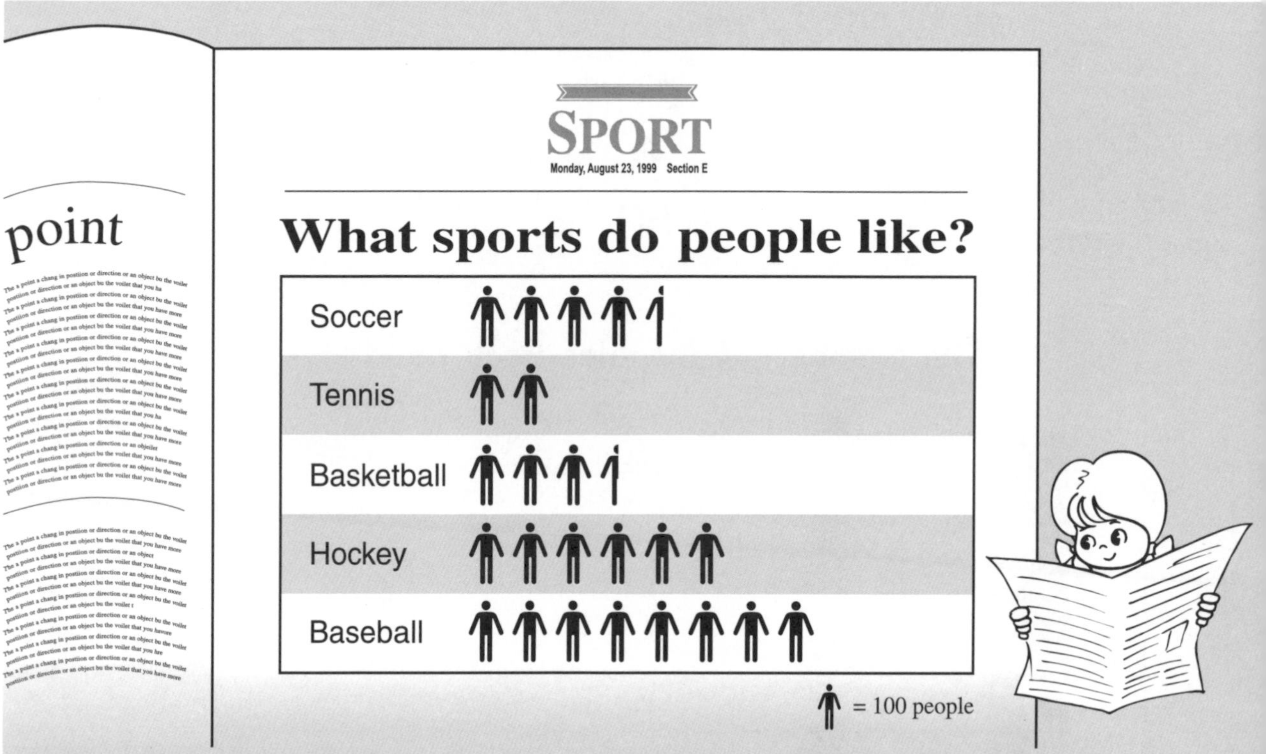

SPORT
Monday, August 23, 1999   Section E

What sports do people like?

Soccer	🚶🚶🚶🚶🚶
Tennis	🚶🚶
Basketball	🚶🚶🚶🚶
Hockey	🚶🚶🚶🚶🚶🚶
Baseball	🚶🚶🚶🚶🚶🚶🚶🚶

🚶 = 100 people

⑭ How many people are represented by 🚶 ? _____

⑮ How many people are represented by 🚶 ? _____

⑯ How many people like baseball? _____

⑰ How many more people like hockey than soccer? _____

Study the circle graph below. Then tick ✔ the right answers.

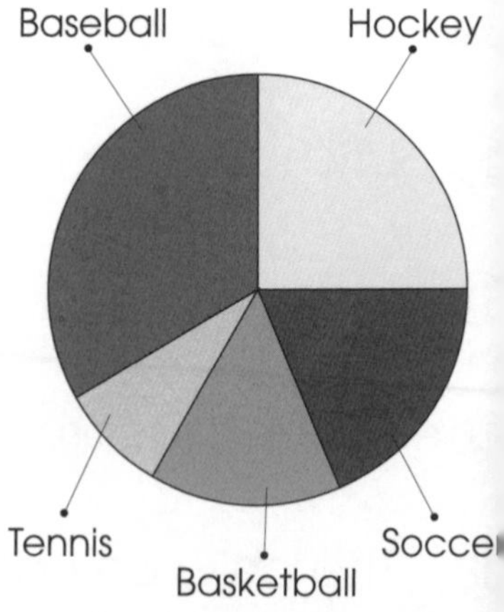

⑱ Which sport do most people like?

☐ Hockey   ☐ Soccer   ☐ Baseball

⑲ About how many of the people like baseball?

☐ $\frac{1}{2}$ ☐ $\frac{1}{3}$ ☐ $\frac{1}{4}$

⑳ Do more people like basketball or hockey?

☐ Basketball   ☐ Hockey

Baseball   Hockey

Tennis   Soccer

Basketball

Read the newspaper to see what the people like to play. Then tick ✔ the right answers.

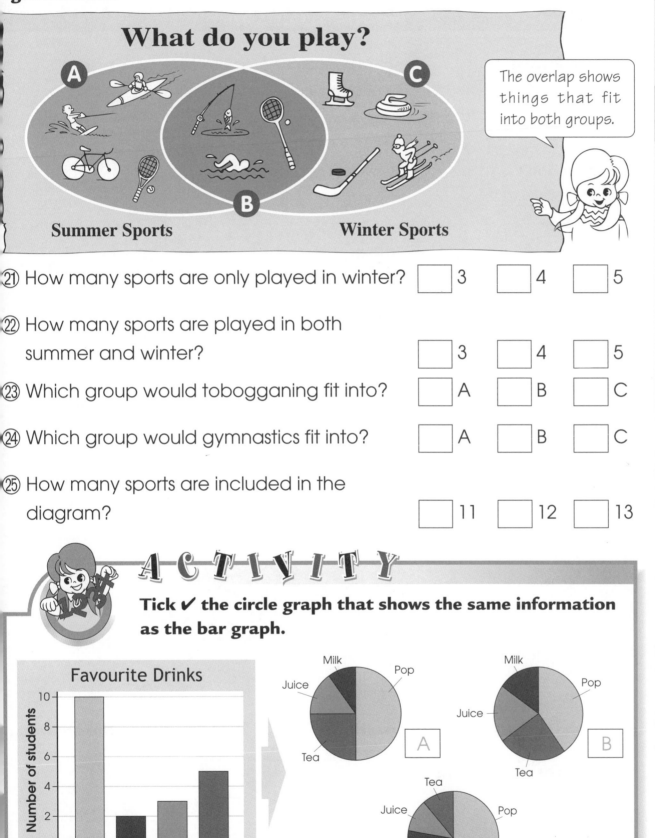

What do you play?

A

C

The overlap shows things that fit into both groups.

B

Summer Sports   **Winter Sports**

㉑ How many sports are only played in winter? ☐ 3   ☐ 4   ☐ 5

㉒ How many sports are played in both summer and winter? ☐ 3   ☐ 4   ☐ 5

㉓ Which group would tobogganing fit into? ☐ A   ☐ B   ☐ C

㉔ Which group would gymnastics fit into? ☐ A   ☐ B   ☐ C

㉕ How many sports are included in the diagram? ☐ 11   ☐ 12   ☐ 13

ACTIVITY

Tick ✔ the circle graph that shows the same information as the bar graph.

Favourite Drinks

Number of students

10
8
6
4
2

Pop   Milk   Juice   Tea
Drinks

Milk   Pop
Juice
Tea
A

Milk
Pop
Juice
Tea
B

Tea
Juice   Pop
Milk
C

21 Transformations and Grid

Transformation	-	a change in position or direction of an object by sliding, flipping or turning
Translation	-	sliding up, down or sideways
Reflection	-	flipping over a line
Rotation	-	turning about a point
Grid	-	a system of numbered squares on a map for finding the exact position of an object or a place

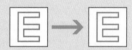

turn point $\frac{1}{4}$ turn clockwise

e.g.

The ♥ is in the square (3,2).

Write slide, flip or turn.

①

②

③

④

Read what Nancy says. Do questions ⑤ to ⑨. Write or tick ✔ the answers.

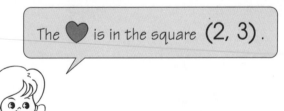

The ♥ is in the square (2, 3).

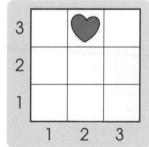

Write the horizontal (→) number first, and then the vertical (↑) number.

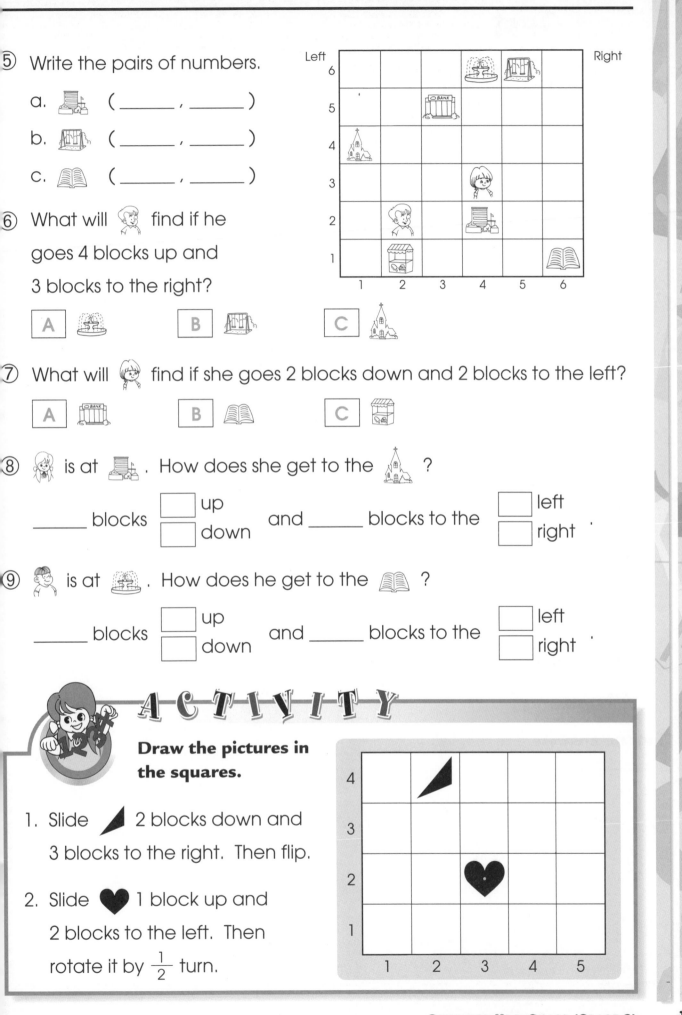

⑤ Write the pairs of numbers.

a. (_____ , _____)

b. (_____ , _____)

c. (_____ , _____)

⑥ What will find if he goes 4 blocks up and 3 blocks to the right?

A | B | C

⑦ What will find if she goes 2 blocks down and 2 blocks to the left?

A | B | C

⑧ is at . How does she get to the ?

_____ blocks ☐ up ☐ down and _____ blocks to the ☐ left ☐ right .

⑨ is at . How does he get to the ?

_____ blocks ☐ up ☐ down and _____ blocks to the ☐ left ☐ right .

ACTIVITY

Draw the pictures in the squares.

1. Slide ◢ 2 blocks down and 3 blocks to the right. Then flip.

2. Slide ♥ 1 block up and 2 blocks to the left. Then rotate it by $\frac{1}{2}$ turn.

Find the factors. (12 marks)

① 18 = 1 x ☐
    = 2 x ☐
    = 3 x ☐
Factors of 18 : _____

② 20 = 1 x ☐
    = 2 x ☐
    = 4 x ☐
Factors of 20 : _____

③ 32 = 1 x ☐
    = 2 x ☐
    = 4 x ☐
Factors of 32 : _____

④ 45 = 1 x ☐
    = 3 x ☐
    = 5 x ☐
Factors of 45 : _____

⑤ Factors of 36 : _____ .

⑥ Factors of 48 : _____ .

Find the answers. (18 marks)

⑦
8) 3 7 6

⑧
5) 7 6 1

⑨
4) 8 2 6

⑩
$$9\overline{)809}$$

⑪
$$2\overline{)321}$$

⑫
$$3\overline{)607}$$

⑬
$$6\overline{)430}$$

⑭
$$7\overline{)342}$$

⑮
$$4\overline{)503}$$

Match the questions that have the same answers. (12 marks)

⑯ $4 \times 10 - 15$ • • $49 + 5 \times 12$

⑰ $163 - 6 \times 9$ • • $120 \div 6 \times 7$

⑱ $70 \div 2 \times 4$ • • $39 \div 3 + 12$

⑲ $39 \times 2 \div 3$ • • $37 \times 4 + 16$

⑳ $135 \div 9 \times 4$ • • $116 - 8 \times 7$

㉑ $116 + 96 \div 2$ • • $59 \times 2 - 92$

Find the total amount and the change for each group. (8 marks)

$ 4.35 $ 1.25 $ 0.99 $ 0.94 $ 2.65 $ 1.07

Total	Money given	Change

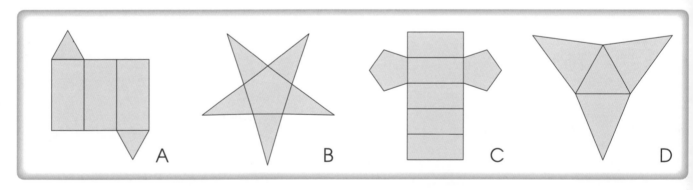

㉒ ♥ $4.35
       $.
    +$.
       $.

Money given

Change
$.
−$.
$.

㉓ 🌷 $.
        $.
     +$.
        $.

$.
−$.
$.

Match the nets with the right pyramids or prisms. Write the letters only. (4 marks)

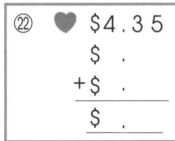 A    B   C   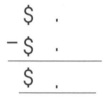 D

㉔ 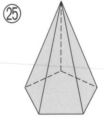   ㉕ 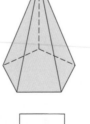   ㉖    ㉗

[ ]   [ ]   [ ]   [ ]

Write the fractions. (3 marks)

㉘ oranges

___

㉙ apples

___

㉚ strawberries

___

Write the fractions of the shaded parts. (2 marks)

㉛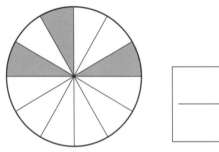

___

㉜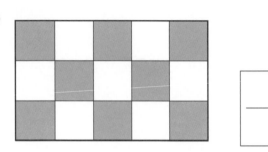

___

Do the problems. (6 marks)

㉝ $\dfrac{3}{4} - \dfrac{1}{4} =$ ___

㉞ $\dfrac{5}{7} + \dfrac{1}{7} =$ ___

㉟ $\dfrac{4}{10} - \dfrac{2}{10} =$ ___

㊱ $\dfrac{9}{10} + \dfrac{1}{10} = \dfrac{\quad}{10} =$ ___

㊲ $\dfrac{5}{6} - \dfrac{3}{6} =$ ___

㊳ $\dfrac{7}{8} + \dfrac{1}{8} = \dfrac{\quad}{8} =$ ___

If Nancy empties all the water into the pail, how full will the pail be? Draw the water level. (2 marks)

㊴

 1L 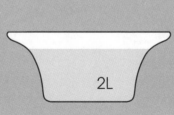 2L 2L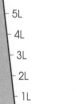

5L
4L
3L
2L
1L

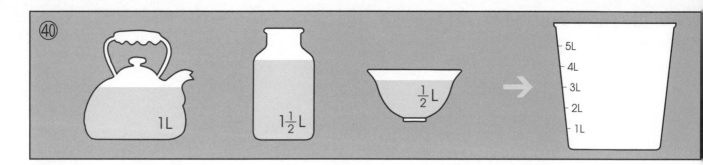

Finish the patterns. (4 marks)

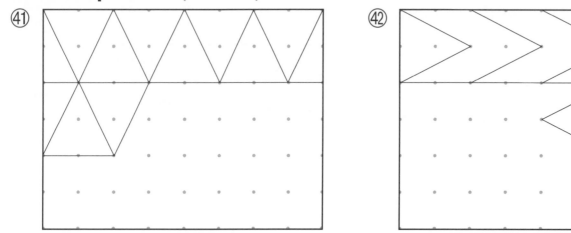

Tick ✔ the shapes that can make a tile pattern. (3 marks)

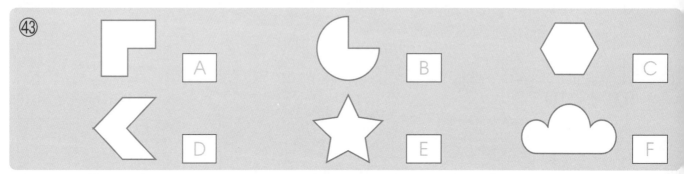

How many lines of symmetry are there? Write the numbers. (6 marks)

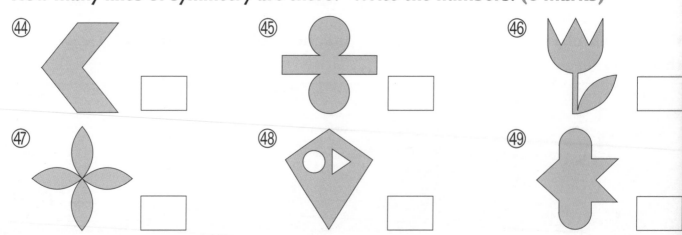

Colour the boxes to complete the bar graph. Then fill in the blanks. (12 marks)

㊿

Number of gumballs	
Nancy	‖‖‖ ‖‖‖ ‖‖‖ ‖‖‖ ‖‖‖ ‖‖‖ ‖‖‖ ‖‖‖
Mark	‖‖‖ ‖‖‖ ‖‖‖ ‖‖‖ ‖‖‖ ‖‖‖
Jill	‖‖‖ ‖‖‖ ‖‖‖ ‖‖‖ ‖‖‖
Peter	‖‖‖ ‖‖‖ ‖‖‖ ‖‖‖ ‖‖‖ ‖‖‖
George	‖‖‖ ‖‖‖ ‖‖‖ ‖‖‖

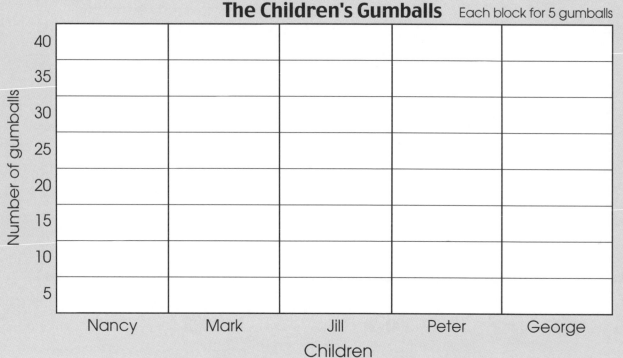

The Children's Gumballs   Each block for 5 gumballs

(bar graph with vertical axis "Number of gumballs" marked 5, 10, 15, 20, 25, 30, 35, 40 and horizontal axis "Children" with Nancy, Mark, Jill, Peter, George)

(51) Peter has _____ gumballs.

(52) Mark has as many gumballs as _____ .

(53) _____ has the most gumballs.

(54) Jill has more gumballs than _____ . She has _____ more.

(55) Nancy and Mark have _____ gumballs in all.

(56) The children have _____ gumballs in all.

Look at the grid. Write the numbers and tick ✔ the right answers. (6 marks)

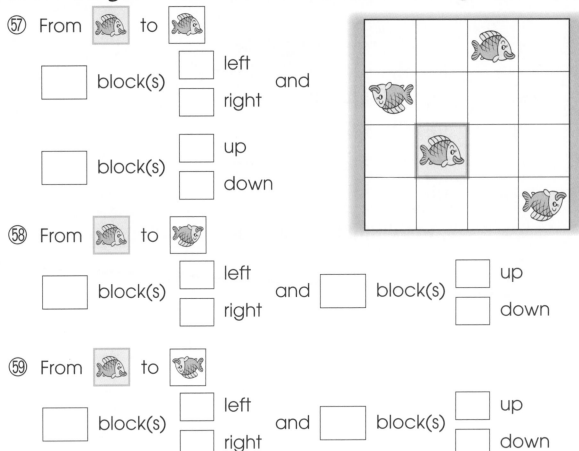

㊹ 57 From [fish] to [fish]

[ ] block(s)   [ ] left   and
                [ ] right

[ ] block(s)   [ ] up
                [ ] down

㊹ 58 From [fish] to [fish]

[ ] block(s)   [ ] left   and   [ ] block(s)   [ ] up
                [ ] right   [ ] down

㊹ 59 From [fish] to [fish]

[ ] block(s)   [ ] left   and   [ ] block(s)   [ ] up
                [ ] right   [ ] down

Match the bar graphs with the circle graphs. Write the letters. (2 marks)

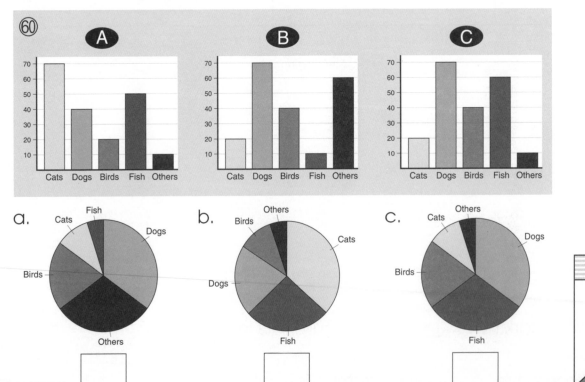

Section IV

Overview

In this section, the skills developed in previous units are consolidated through practice in word problems.

Emphasis is placed on careful reading and showing the steps in calculation. Calculators may be used for some of the more complex money applications and children are encouraged to round off numbers and estimate answers before calculating exact answers.

At the end of each unit, there is an additional question to provide extra challenge.

UNIT 1 Numeration

EXAMPLE

Jack is 132 cm tall and Jill is 146 cm tall. Who is taller?

Compare the
hundreds digit

1 3 2

1 4 6

If they are the
same, then

Compare the
tens digit

1 3 2

1 4 6

4 is greater than 3, so
146 > 132

Answer : Jill is taller than Jack.

Here are some students in Mrs Winter's class. Use the table to find the answers.

Student	Joe	Ann	Lesley	Paul	Gary	Joan
Height (cm)	134	145	120	130	125	144

① Write the names in order of height from the shortest to the tallest.

Answer : _____ , _____ , _____ , _____ , _____ ,

② If Lesley has grown 10 cm every year for the past 4 years, complete the table to show her height.

	1 year ago	2 years ago	3 years ago	4 years ago
Height (cm)				

③ How many centimetres would Paul have to grow to be as tall as Ann?

Answer : _____

④ What is the difference in height between the tallest student and the shortest student?

Answer : _____

Mrs Winter's class is having a marble competition.   Read the table and answer the questions.

Students	Joe	Ann	Lesley	Paul	Gary
Number of marbles	513	310	413	523	270

⑤ Write the names in order from the student that has the most marbles to the student that has the fewest.

Answer : _____

⑥ Who has 100 fewer marbles than Joe?

Answer : _____

⑦ Who has 40 more marbles than Gary?

Answer : _____

⑧ If you count up in 5's from the number of marbles Gary has, whose number will you get to first?

Answer : _____

⑨ Who can match another person's score by winning 10 marbles?

Answer : _____

CHALLENGE

If Gary is playing against Ann, how many marbles must Ann give to Gary for them to have the same number? Show your work and explain.

Answer : _____

UNIT  **Addition and Subtraction**

EXAMPLE

A pond has 12 ducks on it. If 10 more fly in, how many ducks are there altogether?

Think : `Add' words - more, altogether, join, in all

 `Subtract' words - left, fewer, fly away

Write :   12 + 10 = 22

Answer :   There are 22 ducks altogether.

Use this picture of a farm to answer the questions.

① How many animals are there in all?

Answer: There are   animals in all.

② How many 4-legged animals are there?

Answer:

③ If 15 more ducks come to the pond, how many ducks are there altogether?

Answer:

④ How many animals with wings are there?

Answer:

⑤ If there are 20 cows on the farm, how many cows are still in the barn?

Answer:

⑥ In the picture, how many more 4-legged animals are there than 2-legged ones?

Answer:

Solve the problems. Show your work.

⑦ Peter has 39 goats. He wants to have 64 goats. How many more goats should he buy?

Answer: _____

⑧ Peter has 68 animals on his farm. He buys 23 more. How many animals does he have now?

Answer: _____

⑨ Peter has 24 ducks, 34 geese and 59 chickens. How many birds does he have?

Answer: _____

⑩ Peter sold 47 cows and 59 goats. How many cows and goats did Peter sell altogether?

Answer: _____

⑪ There are 196 gulls in Peter's field. 98 of them fly away but 105 more gulls arrive. How many gulls are there altogether?

Answer: _____

⑫ After 312 gulls have gone, there are 64 left. How many gulls were there at the start?

Answer: _____

⑬ There are 305 gulls but 84 of them fly away. How many gulls are left?

Answer: _____

⑭ There are 576 gulls, but 153 fly away. Then 283 more leave. How many gulls remain?

Answer: _____

⑮ 413 gulls are joined by 311 more. Then 136 more gulls come. How many gulls are there altogether?

Answer: _____

Steps for solving problems: ← Read this first.

1. *Write down the facts.*
2. *Decide what operations to use.*
3. *Calculate.*
4. *Write the answer.*

Read the inventory of Peter's animals. Write the names of the animals.

Sheep 54	Pigs 58	Ducks 67
Goats 104	Cows 42	Chickens....121

⑯ I have about 70 _____ .

⑰ I have about 40 _____ .

⑱ I have about 120 _____ .

⑲ I have about 100 _____ .

⑳ I have about 50 _____ .

㉑ I have about 60 _____ .

Look at Peter's fields and solve the problems. Show your work.

A

B

C

D

25 trees

50 trees

150 trees

100 trees

㉒ Peter wants to plant 48 apple trees in one of these fields. Which field should he use? Explain.

Answer: _____

㉓ If Peter plants 68 cherry trees in field C, how many more trees can he plant there afterwards?

Answer: _____

㉔ If Peter plants 68 cherry plants in fields A and B, how many more trees can he plant there afterwards?

Answer: _____

㉕ Peter has 53 apple trees and 75 cherry trees. If he plants them in the same field, which field should he choose? Explain.

Answer: _____

㉖ How many more trees can Peter plant there?

Answer: _____

㉗ Peter has 91 peach trees in field D. If 36 of these are chopped down, how many more trees can he plant there?

Answer: _____

CHALLENGE

Peter has some ducks and some sheep on his farm. He counts 9 animals and 32 legs. How many ducks and sheep are there? Prove your answer with a picture.

Answer: _____

Multiplication

EXAMPLE

There are 3 groups of 5 children at the camp. How many children are there altogether?

Think : Multiplication is repeated addition.

Write : $3 \times 5 = 15$ is $5 + 5 + 5 = 15$

Answer : There are 15 children altogether.

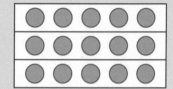

Follow Peter's method to complete the following table.

	Diagram	Multiplication sentence	Number of chips
① 5 cookies with 4 chocolate chips each	🍪 🍪 🍪 🍪 🍪	5×4	20
② 5 cookies with 6 chocolate chips each			
③ 3 cookies with 4 chocolate chips each			
④ 4 cookies with 7 chocolate chips each			
⑤ 3 cookies with 5 chocolate chips each			
⑥ 6 cookies with 2 chocolate chips each			

Write a sentence to describe each picture. Then use multiplication to find how many fruits there are in all.

⑦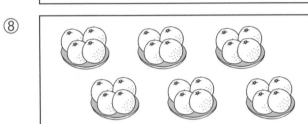

5 plates with _____ apples each.

5 × 3 = _____

There are _____ apples in all.

⑧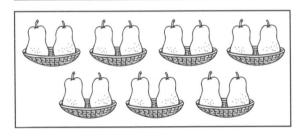

_____

_____

_____

⑨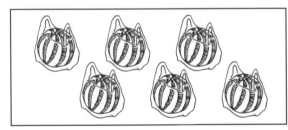

_____

_____

_____

⑩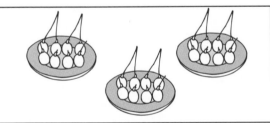

_____

_____

_____

⑪

_____

_____

_____

_____

Solve the problems. Show your work.

⑫ If each box holds 8 apples, how many apples are there in 6 boxes?

Answer: _____

⑬ If each bag holds 7 oranges, how many oranges are there in 9 bags?

Answer: _____

Find how many snacks each group of children will get in all. Show your work.

1 ⬭ for each person

Cookies

Crackers

Marshmallows

Brownies

Chicken nuggets

Candies

Cheese sticks

Pretzels

⑭ We like candies.

Answer : 3 children will get _____ candies in all.

⑮ We want crackers.

Answer : _____

⑯ We want chicken nuggets.

Answer : _____

⑰ We like cookies.

Answer : _____

⑱ We like cheese sticks.

Answer : _____

⑲

We like brownies.

Answer : _____

⑳

We like marshmallows.

Answer : _____

㉑

We like pretzels.

Answer : _____

㉒ If each cookie has 6 chocolate chips, how many chips are there on a plate of cookies?

Answer : _____

㉓ If each cracker has 2 pieces of cheese, how many pieces are there on a plate of crackers?

Answer : _____

㉔ If each marshmallow weighs 5 grams, how many grams of marshmallows are there on a plate?

Answer : _____

㉕ If a candy costs 6¢, how much does a plate of candies cost?

Answer : _____

CHALLENGE

Terry put 2 nickels into his piggy bank on the first day, 4 nickels on the second day and 6 nickels on the third day. How many cents has Terry saved?

Answer: _____

EXAMPLE

Joe has 15 cupcakes at his party. If there are 5 children, how many cupcakes will each child get?

Think : How many groups of 5 are there in 15?

Write : $15 \div 5 = 3$

Answer : Each child will get 3 cupcakes.

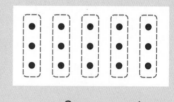

Circle each share of snacks. Then complete the division sentences and write the statements.

① Divide 10 cupcakes among 5 children. How many cupcakes will each child get?

$10 \div 5 =$ _____

Answer: Each child will get _____ cupcakes.

② 3 boys share 12 cookies equally. How many cookies will each boy get?

$12 \div$ _____ $=$ _____

Answer:

③ Divide 20 candies into 5 groups. How many candies are there in each group?

_____ $\div$ _____ $=$ _____

Answer:

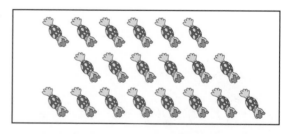

④ Divide 18 crackers among 6 children. How many crackers will each child get?

_____ $\div$ _____ $=$ _____

Answer:

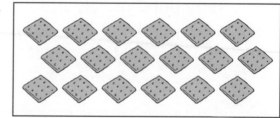

Mrs Winter puts 24 doughnuts into baskets. Write the division sentences and statements.

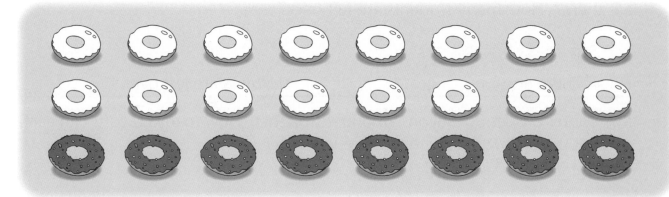

⑤ If Mrs Winter puts 3 doughnuts in each basket, how many baskets does she need?

Answer: She needs _____ baskets.

⑥ If Mrs Winter puts 4 doughnuts in each basket, how many baskets does she need ?

Answer: _____

⑦ If Mrs Winter puts 6 doughnuts in each basket, how many baskets does she need ?

Answer: _____

⑧ If Mrs Winter puts 8 doughnuts in each basket, how many baskets does she need ?

Answer: _____

⑨ There are 8 chocolate doughnuts and 16 honey doughnuts. Mrs Winter makes 2 groups with the same number of chocolate doughnuts and honey doughnuts in each group. How many chocolate doughnuts are there in each group?

Answer: _____

⑩ How many honey doughnuts are there in each group?

Answer: _____

⑪ Mrs Winter makes 4 groups with the same number of chocolate doughnuts and honey doughnuts in each group. How many chocolate doughnuts and honey doughnuts are there in each group?

Answer: _____

Solve the problems. Show your work.

⑫ Mrs Winter divides her class of 24 students into groups of 5. How many groups are there? How many students are left over?

Answer: There are _____ groups, and _____ students are left over.

⑬ Mrs Winter divides 30 crayons among 4 students. How many crayons can each student get? How many crayons are left over?

Answer:

⑭ Mrs Winter divides 48 markers among 9 students. How many markers can each student get? How many markers are left over?

Answer:

⑮ Mrs Winter divides 61 markers among 7 students. How many markers can each student get? How many markers are left over?

Answer:

⑯ Mrs Winter has 6 pencils and 8 rulers. If she wants each student to have 2 pencils and 1 ruler, how many students can she give them to?

Answer:

⑰ Mrs Winter has 19 erasers and 7 glue sticks. If she wants each student to have 2 erasers and 1 glue stick, how many students can she give them to?

Answer:

⑱ How many erasers and glue sticks are left over?

Answer:

Read the story and solve the problems.

Joe brought some cupcakes to school on his birthday. The cupcakes came in packages of 4 and 6.

⑲ How many small boxes would he need to hold 36 cupcakes?

Answer: _____

⑳ How many big boxes would he need to hold 36 cupcakes?

Answer: _____

㉑ How many small boxes would he need to hold 48 cupcakes?

Answer: _____

㉒ If Joe had 18 cupcakes, how many small boxes would he need?

Answer: _____

㉓ If Joe had 26 cupcakes, how many small boxes would he need?

Answer: _____

㉔ If Joe had 26 cupcakes, how many big boxes would he need?

Answer: _____

CHALLENGE

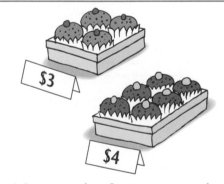

① How many small boxes would you buy to have 12 cupcakes? How much would you have to pay for them?

Answer: _____

② How many big boxes would you buy to have 12 cupcakes? How much would you have to pay for them?

Answer: _____

③ Which do you think is a better deal? Explain.

Answer: _____

UNIT 5 — Fractions

EXAMPLE

Ann divided her pizza into 4 equal parts and ate 1 part. What fraction of Ann's pizza was eaten?

One out of four parts of the pizza was eaten.

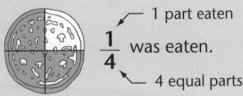

$\dfrac{1}{4}$ was eaten.

— 1 part eaten

— 4 equal parts

Answer : $\dfrac{1}{4}$ of Ann's pizza was eaten.

- *A fraction is a part of something that has been divided into equal parts.*

Read this first.

Write the numbers and fractions to complete the sentences. Then colour the eaten part of each pizza.

①
Joe divided his pizza into _____ parts.

2 out of _____ parts of Joe's pizza were eaten.

$\dfrac{2}{\boxed{}}$ of Joe's pizza was eaten.

②
Sarah divided her pizza into _____ parts.

5 out of _____ parts of Sarah's pizza were eaten.

$\boxed{}$ of Sarah's pizza was eaten.

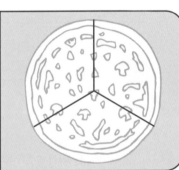

③
Martin divided his pizza into _____ parts.

3 out of _____ parts of Martin's pizza were eaten.

$\boxed{}$ of Martin's pizza was eaten.

Look at Ann's groceries. Write a statement to answer each question.

④ What fraction of the groceries are bags?

Answer: _____ of the groceries are bags. _____

⑤ What fraction of the groceries are cans?

Answer: _____

⑥ What fraction of the groceries are 🛍 ?

Answer: _____

⑦ What fraction of the groceries are 🥫 ?

Answer: _____

⑧ What fraction of the bags are 🛍 ?

Answer: _____

⑨ What fraction of the cans are 🥫 ?

Answer: _____

⑩ If Ann wanted $\frac{1}{2}$ of the groceries to be in bags, how many more bags would she need?

Answer: _____

⑪ If Ann wanted $\frac{1}{2}$ of the groceries to be in cans, how many cans would she take away?

Answer: _____

Answer the questions. Then follow the answers to colour the string of beads.

⑫ 4 beads out of 6 are yellow. What fraction of the beads are yellow?

Answer: _____ of the beads are yellow.

⑬ 2 beads out of 6 are red. What fraction of the beads are red?

Answer: _____

⑭ Colour the beads.

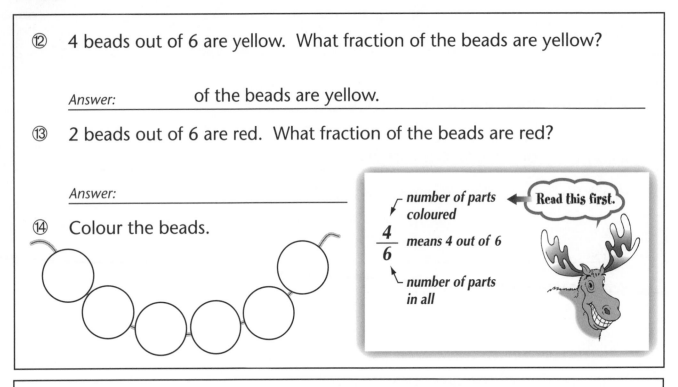

$\frac{4}{6}$ ← number of parts coloured

means 4 out of 6

← number of parts in all

Read this first.

⑮ 6 beads out of 12 are red. What fraction of the beads are red?

Answer: _____

⑯ 2 beads out of 12 are yellow. What fraction of the beads are yellow?

Answer: _____

⑰ 3 beads out of 12 are blue. What fraction of the beads are blue?

Answer: _____

⑱ 1 bead out of 12 is orange. What fraction of the beads are orange?

Answer: _____

⑲ Colour the beads.

Read the table and answer the questions.

	Pop		Juice	
Flavour	Orange	Grape	Orange	Grape
Number of drinks	8	3	4	5

⑳ What fraction of the drinks are pop?

Answer: _____

• First, find how many drinks Ann has bought in all.

Read this first.

㉑ What fraction of the drinks are juice?

Answer: _____

㉒ What fraction of the juices are orange flavour?

Answer: _____

㉔ What fraction of the drinks are grape flavour?

Answer: _____

㉓ What fraction of the pops are orange flavour?

Answer: _____

㉕ What fraction of the drinks are orange flavour?

Answer: _____

CHALLENGE

Ann's Mom says, 'I have $\frac{1}{3}$, $\frac{1}{5}$ and $\frac{1}{4}$ of a pizza left'. Who should choose which piece?

① Rachel is very hungry. .... 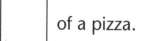 of a pizza.

② Ann is hungry. .... 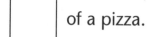 of a pizza.

③ John is not hungry. .... 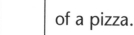 of a pizza.

EXAMPLE

Natasha bought a candy bar for $0.60. She used 3 coins to pay for the exact amount. Which coins did she use?

Think : Use the highest value of the coins possible. Try quarters and dimes.

Write : $0.25 + $0.25 + $0.10 = $0.60

Answer : Natasha used 2 quarters and 1 dime.

Each child paid the exact amount for the following items. Write the number sentences and statements.

① Joe used 2 coins to buy a balloon for $0.30. Which coins did he use?

    Answer: Joe used   quarter(s) and   nickel(s).

② Katherine used 4 coins to buy an ice cream for $2.03. Which coins did she use?

    Answer: _____

③ William used 4 coins to buy a bundle of flowers for $3.15. Which coins did he use?

    Answer: _____

④ Ann used 6 coins to buy a box of chocolates for $1.81. Which coins did she use?

    Answer: _____

⑤ Natasha used 5 coins to buy 2 hot dogs for $2.20 each. Which coins did she use?

> • For question 5, find the total amount Natasha had to pay first. ← Read this first.

    Answer:

The chart shows the prices of food and drinks at a snack bar. Answer the children's questions. Show your work.

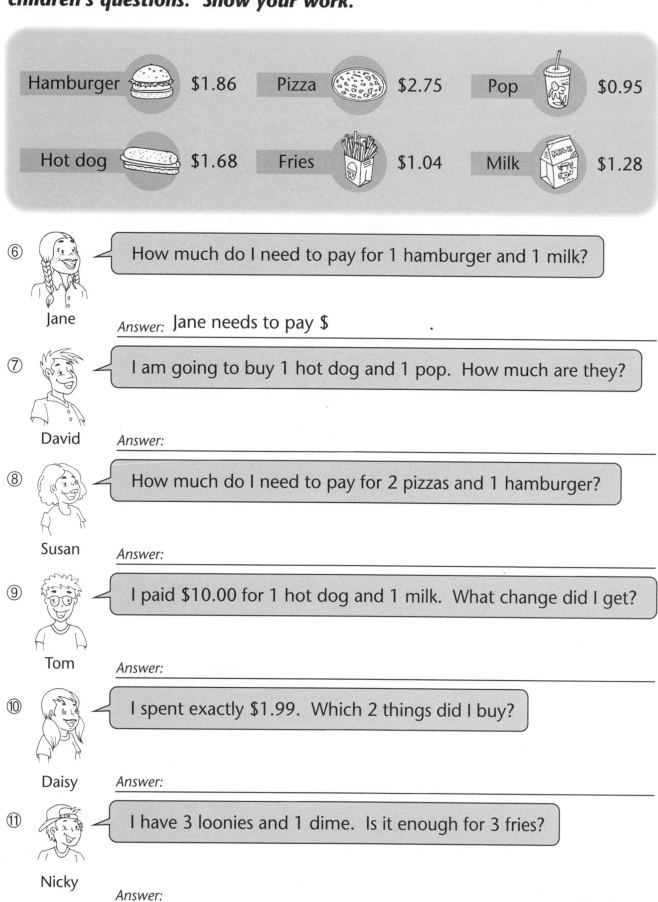

Hamburger	$1.86	Pizza	$2.75	Pop	$0.95
Hot dog	$1.68	Fries	$1.04	Milk	$1.28

⑥ Jane: How much do I need to pay for 1 hamburger and 1 milk?

Answer: Jane needs to pay $ _____ .

⑦ David: I am going to buy 1 hot dog and 1 pop. How much are they?

Answer:

⑧ Susan: How much do I need to pay for 2 pizzas and 1 hamburger?

Answer:

⑨ Tom: I paid $10.00 for 1 hot dog and 1 milk. What change did I get?

Answer:

⑩ Daisy: I spent exactly $1.99. Which 2 things did I buy?

Answer:

⑪ Nicky: I have 3 loonies and 1 dime. Is it enough for 3 fries?

Answer:

Help the cashier give the change to each child with the fewest coins. Show your work.

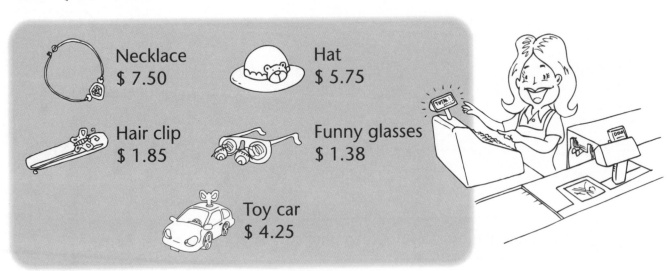

Necklace $ 7.50

Hat $ 5.75

Hair clip $ 1.85

Funny glasses $ 1.38

Toy car $ 4.25

⑫ Joan bought a necklace. What was her change from a $10 bill? What are the coins?

Answer: Joan's change was $ _____ . The coins are _____ twoonie(s) and _____ quarter(s).

⑬ David bought a hat. What was his change from $7.00? What are the coins?

Answer: _____

⑭ Raymond bought 2 toy cars. What was his change from a $10 bill? What are the coins?

Answer: _____

⑮ Lily bought 2 hair clips. What was her change from a $5 bill? What are the coins?

Answer: _____

⑯ Daisy bought 1 pair of funny glasses, 1 hair clip and 1 hat. What was her change from a $10 bill? What are the coins?

Answer: _____

Estimate the value of each item. Round each value to the nearest dollar. Then use your calculator to find the exact total for each bill.

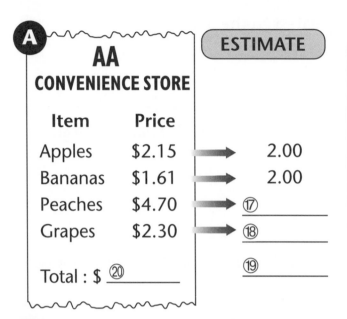

A

AA CONVENIENCE STORE

Item	Price		ESTIMATE
Apples	$2.15	→	2.00
Bananas	$1.61	→	2.00
Peaches	$4.70	→	⑰
Grapes	$2.30	→	⑱
			⑲

Total : $ ⑳

- To find the total for each bill on a calculator, press the keys in order.

For example,
$1.47 + $0.52

| 1 | . | 4 | 7 | + | 0 | . | 5 | 2 | = |

Your answer should be $1.99.

Read this first.

B

AA CONVENIENCE STORE

Item	Price		ESTIMATE
Chips	$1.43	→	㉑
Pops	$6.43	→	㉒
Dressing	$2.80	→	㉓
Bread	$2.25	→	㉔
			㉕

Total : $ ㉖

C

AA CONVENIENCE STORE

Item	Price		ESTIMATE
Pies	$3.20	→	㉗
Brownies	$5.37	→	㉘
Cookies	$2.81	→	㉙
Crackers	$1.09	→	㉚
			㉛

Total : $ ㉜

CHALLENGE

If Jessie paid $20.00 for bill A, Wendy paid $15.00 for bill B and Brian paid $13.00 for bill C, who would get the most change back?

Answer: _____

MIDWAY REVIEW

Here is the amount of money that Joan and her friends have. Joan has $2.50, Ann $1.75, Sue $3.30, John $1.50 and Jane $2.70.

① Write these values in order from the greatest to the least.

Answer : _____

② If Joan wants to buy 2 popsicles for 80¢ each, how much change will she get from $2.00?

Answer : _____

③ Which of these would be the change if Joan's mother paid for her 2 popiscles with a $5 bill?

Answer : _____

④ If Joan changes all her money into quarters, how many quarters can she get? Show the answer with a picture.

Answer : _____

⑤ If Joan splits her quarters into 5 groups, how many quarters will there be in each group? How much money will there be in each group?

Answer : _____

⑥ If Ann earns 75¢ each week, how long will it take her to earn $2.25?

Answer : _____

Look at Ann's collection of marbles.

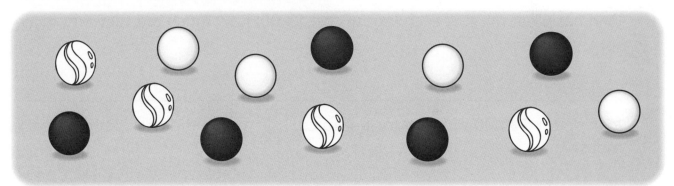

⑦ How many marbles does Ann have?

Answer : _____

⑧ If Ann is given 29 marbles, how many will she have altogether?

Answer : _____

⑨ What fraction of the marbles are black?

Answer : _____

⑩ What fraction of the marbles have a cat's eye?

Answer : _____

⑪ If Ann lost 8 marbles, how many would she have?

Answer : _____

⑫ How many black marbles would Ann have to buy so she would have $\frac{1}{2}$ of her marbles in black?

Answer : _____

⑬ If Ann wants to share her marbles with 2 of her friends, how many marbles will each child get? How many marbles will be left over?

Answer : _____

Solve the problems. Show your work.

⑭ Joan has 6 pet mice. If each mouse cost $3.00, how much did they cost in all?

Answer : _____

⑮ Joan spent $24.00 on food for her mice, how much did she spend on each mouse?

Answer : _____

⑯ 2 of Joan's mice each had 4 babies, and she gave 2 of them to a friend. How many baby mice were left?

Answer : _____

⑰ Each of Joan's mice can sell for $5.00. If she sells 5 of them, how much money will she get?

Answer : _____

⑱ How many would Joan need to sell to have $40.00?

Answer : _____

⑲ Joan has $7.00 to buy toys for the mice. Which three of the toys should she choose to spend exactly $7.00?

Ball  Wheel  Ladder  Tunnel

$3.25 $4.25 $1.75 $2.00

Answer : _____

⑳ Joan bought a ball and a wheel, how much change would she get from $9.00?

Answer : _____

Circle the correct answer in each problem.

㉑ Ann earns $2.00 a week. How long will it take her to save $10.00 if she spends $1.00 each week?

    A. 5 weeks   B. 10 weeks   C. 15 weeks   D. 8 weeks

㉒ Joan and Ann share 24 marbles equally. How many will each get?

    A. 9   B. 10   C. 11   D. 12

㉓ If John joined Joan and Ann, how many should the girls each give up so that they would all have the same number of marbles?

    A. 3   B. 4   C. 6   D. 8

㉔ If John has 10 marbles and Joan has 18 marbles, how many should Joan give to John so that they would have the same number of marbles?

    A. 4   B. 5   C. 6   D. 7

㉕ Joan has 15 dollars. She wants to spend $\frac{1}{3}$ of her money on candies. How much will she have left?

    A. $5.00   B. $10.00   C. $12.00   D. $14.00

㉖ John has $20.00. He spent $5.00 on candies and $3.00 on toys. How much has he spent?

    A. $$\$\frac{8}{20}$$ B. $$\$\frac{12}{20}$$ C. $$\$\frac{3}{5}$$ D. $$\$\frac{5}{23}$$

㉗ Joan has $4.00 and Ann has $12.00. If they each spend $\frac{1}{4}$ of their money, how much will they spend altogether?

    A. $2.00   B. $3.00   C. $4.00   D. $5.00

㉘ How much more money does Ann spend than Joan?

    A. $1.00   B. $2.00   C. $3.00   D. $4.00

EXAMPLE

Units of measuring
capacity   : Litre (L), Millilitre (mL) | 1 L = 1000 mL |

Units of measuring
mass   : Kilogram (kg), Gram (g) | 1 kg = 1000 g |

The capacity of this carton is 1L.

A litre of milk has a mass of about 1kg.

Solve the problems. Show your work.

This jug holds 1 L and 4 jugs fill this bucket .

① What is the capacity of the bucket?

Answer: The capacity is _____ L.

② How much water can 5 jugs hold?

Answer: _____

③ How much water can fill 3 buckets?

Answer: _____

④ How much water can fill 1 jug and 1 bucket?

Answer: _____

⑤ How many millilitres of water can 2 jugs hold?

Answer: _____

⑥ Which hold more, 2 buckets or 5 jugs?

Answer: _____

⑦ Jane fills 3 buckets with water. How many jugs can she fill with the same amount of water?

Answer: _____

Use the pictures to find how much water each container can hold and answer the questions. Show your work.

Containers	Capacity
⑧ vase	L
⑨ bottle	L
⑩ pot	L

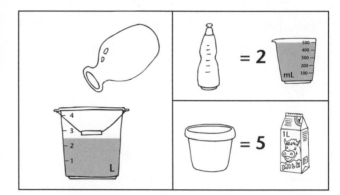

⑪ How much water can 2 vases hold?

Answer: _____

⑫ How much water can 4 bottles hold?

Answer: _____

⑬ How much water can 2 pots hold?

Answer: _____

⑭ How many vases are needed to hold 10 L of water?

Answer: _____

⑮ How many pots are needed to hold 20 L of water?

Answer: _____

⑯ Which container has the greatest capacity?

Answer: _____

⑰ How much greater is the capacity of a pot than that of a vase?

Answer: _____

⑱ How much greater is the capacity of 3 bottles than that of a vase?

Answer: _____

⑲ How many times more water can a pot hold than a vase?

Answer: _____

⑳ How many millilitres of water can a vase hold?

Answer: _____

Decide whether these sentences are about capacity or mass. Write C for capacity and M for mass in the boxes.

㉑ Joan pours 2 glasses of lemonade and has $\frac{1}{2}$ jug of lemonade left.

㉓ When Joan adds 1 cup of juice to her cup, it overflows.

㉒ Joan carries 2 bags in each hand so she can balance.

㉔ Joan can balance on a teeter totter with her 2 baby brothers.

Joan is weighing her books. Answer Joan's questions. Show your work.

㉕ What is the mass of a story book?

Answer: _____

㉖ What is the mass of an exercise book?

Answer: _____

㉗ How much heavier is a story book than an exercise book?

Answer: _____

㉘ How many exercise books will have about the same mass as a story book?

Answer: _____

Look at the pictures and answer the questions.

㉙ Which fruit is lighter than a banana?

Answer: _____ is lighter than a banana.

㉚ Which fruit is heavier than a pineapple?

Answer: _____

㉛ Which fruit is heavier than a banana but lighter than an orange?

Answer: _____

㉜ Put the fruits in order from the heaviest to the lightest.

Answer: _____

CHALLENGE

Joan makes about 250 mL of orange juice with 3 oranges. The mass of 3 oranges is about 1 kg.

① If Joan wants to make 1 L of orange juice, how many oranges does she need?

Answer: _____

② To make 1 L of orange juice, how many kilograms of oranges does she need?

Answer: _____

EXAMPLE

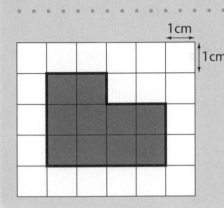

1cm

1cm

What is the perimeter and area of the figure?

Perimeter : 2 + 1 + 2 + 2 + 4 + 3 = 14

Area : It takes 10 ▨ to cover the figure.

Answer : The perimeter of the figure is 14 cm and the area of the figure is 10 cm².

Use the table below to answer the questions.

Pencil	A	B	C	D	E
Length (cm)	5	3	8	12	15

① Which pencil is the longest?

Answer: Pencil _____ is the longest.

② Which pencil is the shortest?

Answer: _____

③ How much longer is pencil C than pencil A?

Answer: _____

④ How much shorter is pencil B than pencil E?

Answer: _____

⑤ If Jill's pencils get shorter by 1cm each week, how long will it take for pencil A to be the same length as pencil B?

Answer: _____

⑥ How long will it take for pencil E to be the same length as pencil C?

Answer: _____

⑦ If Jill uses pencil D for 7 weeks, how long will it be?

Answer: _____

Find the perimeter of each shape by ruler and answer the questions.

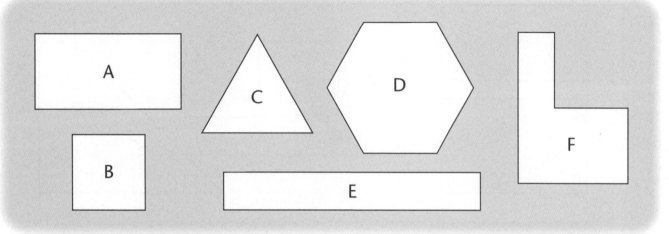

⑧

Shape	A	B	C	D	E	F
Perimeter (cm)						

⑨ Which shape has the greatest perimeter?

Answer:

⑩ Which shape has the smallest perimeter?

Answer:

⑪ Which two of the shapes have the same perimeter?

Answer:

⑫ How much greater is the perimeter of F than that of C?

Answer:

⑬ How many times is the perimeter of E greater than that of B?

Answer:

⑭ Which shape has a greater perimeter than A, but smaller than E?

Answer:

Find the area of each sticker and answer the questions.

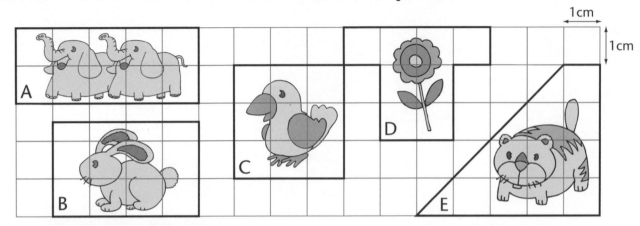

⑮

Sticker	A	B	C	D	E
Area (cm²)					

⑯ Which sticker has the greatest area?

Answer: _____

⑰ Which sticker has the smallest area?

Answer: _____

- 2 ◹ equal to 1 ▪   ← *Read this first.*
  ◹ + ◹ = ▪
- 2 ▭ equal to 1 ▪
  ▭ + ▭ = ▪

⑱ How much smaller is the area of C than that of E?

Answer: _____

⑲ How much greater is the area of B than that of D?

Answer: _____

⑳ Which sticker has a greater area than D, but smaller than A?

Answer: _____

㉑ How many A stickers are needed to cover a piece of paper 4 cm wide and 5 cm long?

Answer: _____

Joan has drawn these shapes on her grid paper. Answer the questions.

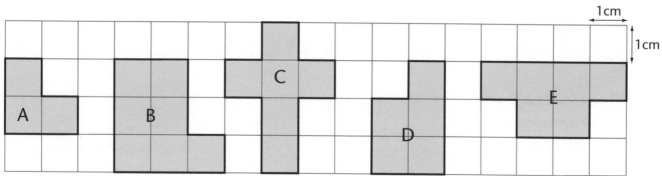

1cm
1cm

㉒ Which shape has the greatest area?

Answer: _____

㉓ Which shape has the greatest perimeter?

Answer: _____

㉔ Which two shapes have the same area?

Answer: _____

㉕ Which two shapes have the same perimeter?

Answer: _____

㉖ How much greater is the area of B than that of A?

Answer: _____

㉗ How much smaller is the perimeter of D than that of C?

Answer: _____

CHALLENGE

A tile is 9 cm long and 6 cm wide. If both its length and width are increased by 2 cm, how much greater is the new perimeter than the old perimeter?

2cm
6cm
9cm   2cm

Answer: _____

EXAMPLE

Which 2 figures would be next in the pattern?

○ ◇ ♡ □ ○ ◇ ♡ □ ○ ◇ ♡ □ ○ ◇ [?] [?]

Think : What is the pattern? What are the figures in the pattern?

The pattern is ○ ◇ ♡ □ .

Answer : The next 2 figures in the pattern are ♡ and □ .

Look at the pattern of Ann's flowers. Answer the questions.

① How many flowers are in a pattern?

Answer: _____ flowers are in a pattern.

② What is the pattern? Draw it.

Answer: _____

③ Which 2 flowers would be next in the pattern?

Answer: _____

④ If Ann picked every 4th flower, which flower would she pick?

Answer: _____

⑤ After picking every 4th flower, how many flowers are in the pattern?

Answer: _____

⑥ What is the new pattern? Draw it.

Answer: _____

⑦ If ⊙ is the first flower in the new pattern, which flower is the second?

Answer: _____

⑧ If ✿ is the third flower in the new pattern, which flower is the first?

Answer: _____

Look at the table showing how tall Ann's flowers have grown. Answer the questions.

Flower	Week 1	Week 2	Week 3	Week 4
(flower 1)	5 cm	10 cm	15 cm	20 cm
(flower 2)	2 cm	4 cm	6 cm	8 cm
(star flower)	4 cm	8 cm	12 cm	16 cm

⑨ Describe the growing pattern of (flower 1).

Answer: It grows _____ every week.

⑩ Find the height of (flower 1) in week 6.

Answer: _____

⑪ Describe the growing pattern of (flower 2).

Answer: _____

⑫ Find the height of (flower 2) in week 6.

Answer: _____

⑬ Describe the growing pattern of (star flower).

Answer: _____

⑭ Find the height of (star flower) in week 6.

Answer: _____

⑮ How long will (flower 1) take to reach a height of 35 cm?

Answer: _____

⑯ How long will (flower 2) take to reach a height of 12 cm?

Answer: _____

⑰ How long will (star flower) take to reach a height of 28 cm?

Answer: _____

Ann and Joan are building towers with blocks. Follow each pattern to add the next set of blocks.

Tower	Step 1	Step 2	Step 3	Step 4
⑱ A				
⑲ B				
⑳ C				

㉑ Complete the chart to show the number of blocks used to build each step of tower A.

4	6	8					

㉒ How many blocks are used in the 10th step to build tower A?

Answer: _____

㉓ Complete the chart to show the number of blocks used to build each step of tower B.

1	4	9					

㉔ How many blocks are used in the 10th step to build tower B?

Answer: _____

㉕ Complete the chart to show the number of blocks used to build each step of tower C.

1	3	6					

㉖ How many blocks are used in the 10th step to build tower C?

Answer: _____

Solve the problems.   Show your work.

5, 10, 15, 20, 25, 30

㉗   What is the rule for this pattern?

Answer: _____

㉘   What are the next 4 numbers?

Answer: _____

256, 258, 260, 262, 264

㉛   What is the rule for this pattern?

Answer: _____

㉜   What are the next 4 numbers?

Answer: _____

120, 110, 100, 90, 80, 70

㉙   What is the rule for this pattern?

Answer: _____

㉚   What are the next 4 numbers?

Answer: _____

919, 819, 719, 619, 519

㉝   What is the rule for this pattern?

Answer: _____

㉞   What are the next 4 numbers?

Answer: _____

CHALLENGE

Joan puts 12¢ in her piggy bank every day.

①   How much has Joan saved on the 6th day?

Answer: _____

②   How long will Joan take to have $1.20?

Answer: _____

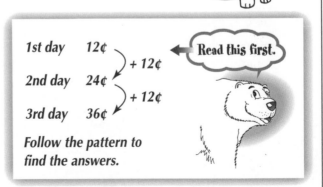

1st day   12¢
                    ⟩ + 12¢
2nd day   24¢
                    ⟩ + 12¢
3rd day   36¢

Follow the pattern to find the answers.

Read this first.

EXAMPLE

What is this solid? How many faces does it have?

Think: This solid has a rectangular base. It is a prism.

Answer: It is a rectangular prism.

Think: Open the solid to find how many faces it has.

Answer: It has 6 faces.

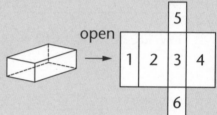

open →

	5		
1	2	3	4
	6		

Complete the table and answer the questions.

A  B C 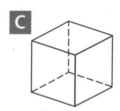 D 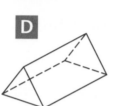 E  F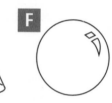

①

Solid	Name
A	
B	
C	
D	
E	
F	

② How many faces does A have?

Answer: A has _____ faces.

③ How many faces does C have?

Answer: _____

④ Which of the solids above has 2 circular faces?

Answer: _____

⑤ Which of the solids above can be stacked?

Answer: _____

⑥ Which of the solids above can roll?

Answer: _____

Complete the table and answer the questions.

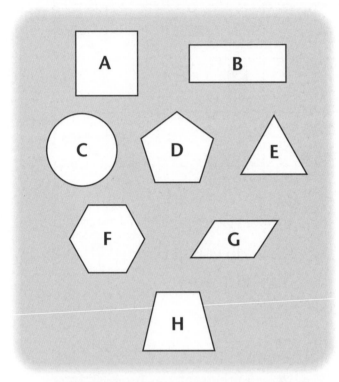

⑦

Shape	Name
A	
B	
C	
D	
E	
F	
G	
H	

⑧ Which of the shapes above has 3 sides?

Answer : _____ has 3 sides.

⑨ Which of the shapes have 4 sides?

Answer : _____

⑩ Which of the shapes have 4 equal sides?

Answer : _____

⑪ How many vertices does F have?

Answer : _____

⑫ How many lines of symmetry are there in a square?

Answer : _____

⑬ How many lines of symmetry are there in a rectangle?

Answer : _____

⑭ Which of the shapes is the top view of a cylinder?

Answer : _____

⑮ If the side view of a triangular prism is B, which one of the shapes is its top view?

Answer : _____

Use the grid to answer the questions.

Left ... Right

⑯ Which of the shapes above is 1 square up and 2 squares to the left of ⋁ ?

Answer : _____

⑰ Which of the shapes above is 3 squares down and 2 squares to the right of ⊤ ?

Answer : _____

⑱ How do you get from ⋁ to ⊣ ?

Answer : _____

⑲ How do you get from ⊤ to β ?

Answer : _____

⑳ How do you get from ⊤ to ◁ ?

Answer : _____

㉑ How do you get from ⊤ to its $\frac{1}{2}$ turned image?

Answer : _____

㉒ How do you get from ⊤ to its slid image?

Answer : _____

㉓ How do you get from ¶ to its flipped image?

Answer : _____

㉔ How do you get from ⋁ to its $\frac{1}{2}$ turned image?

Answer : _____

㉕ How do you get from ⋁ to its $\frac{1}{4}$ clockwise turned image?

Answer : _____

㉖ Which of these shapes are symmetrical : ⬡ , T , ⧙ and V ?

Answer :_____

㉗ How many lines of symmetry does ⬡ have?

Answer :_____

㉘ How many lines of symmetry does T have?

Answer :_____

㉙ How many lines of symmetry does V have?

Answer :_____

㉚ Is ⬡ similar or congruent to ⬡ ?

Answer:_____

㉛ Is T similar or congruent to ⊥ ?

Answer :_____

㉜ Is ⧙ similar or congruent to ⧘ ?

Answer :_____

Read this first.

A B C

- Congruent figures have the same size and shape, e.g. A is congruent to C.

- Similar figures have the same shape, but not the same size, e.g. B is similar to C.

CHALLENGE

① Jill has the same number of triangles as squares. There are 21 sides altogether. How many does Jill have of each?

Answer :_____

② How many lines of symmetry does a circle have?

Answer :_____

UNIT 11 Pictographs

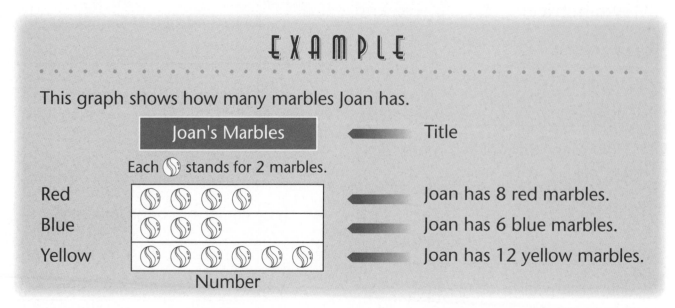

EXAMPLE

This graph shows how many marbles Joan has.

Joan's Marbles ← Title

Each 🔵 stands for 2 marbles.

Red   🔵🔵🔵🔵   ← Joan has 8 red marbles.
Blue   🔵🔵🔵   ← Joan has 6 blue marbles.
Yellow 🔵🔵🔵🔵🔵🔵 ← Joan has 12 yellow marbles.

Number

The graph shows the number of vehicles parked at the Pizza King parking lot yesterday. Use the pictograph to answer the questions.

Each picture stands for 2 vehicles.

① How many cars were parked at the Pizza King parking lot?

   Answer: _____ cars were parked there.

② How many more cars than vans were parked there?

   Answer: _____

③ How many vehicles were parked there ?

   Answer: _____

④ If each van carried 3 people, how many people came to the pizza store by van?

   Answer: _____

The graph shows the number of pizzas ordered yesterday. Use the pictograph to answer the questions.

Number of Pizzas Ordered

Small	🍕 🍕 🍕 🍕 🍕 🍕
Medium	🍕 🍕 🍕 🍕 🍕 🍕 🍕 🍕 🍕
Large	🍕 🍕 🍕 🍕 🍕(half)

Each pizza stands for 2 orders.

⑤ What is the title of this pictograph?

Answer: _____

⑥ How many sizes are there?

Answer: _____

⑦ How many order(s) does 🍕 stand for?

Answer: _____

⑧ How many small pizzas were ordered?

Answer: _____

⑨ How many more medium pizzas were ordered than large pizzas?

Answer: _____

⑩ How many pizzas were ordered in all?

Answer: _____

CHALLENGE

Colour the pictograph to show the number of pizzas ordered.

Kind	No. of Pizzas
Pepperoni	̶I̶I̶I̶I̶ II
Vegetarian	̶I̶I̶I̶I̶ IIII
Hawaiian	IIII

No. of Pizzas Ordered   🍕 = 2 orders

Pepperoni	🍕 🍕 🍕 🍕 🍕
Vegetarian	🍕 🍕 🍕 🍕 🍕
Hawaiian	🍕 🍕 🍕 🍕 🍕

UNIT 12 Bar Graphs

The graph shows the number of stickers collected by the children.

Here are the points to remember :
- Write the title.
- Label the two axes.
- Write the scale.
- Draw the bars with the same width.

The owner of Pizza King used a bar graph to show customers' choice of one-topping pizzas last week. Use his bar graph to answer the questions.

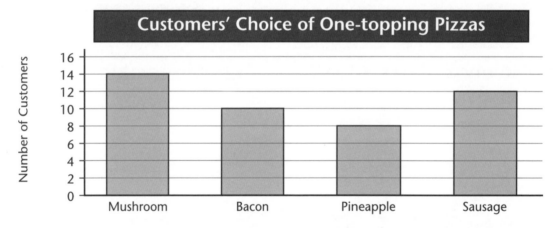

① What is the title of this bar graph?

Answer:

② How many people chose bacon?

Answer:

③ How many people chose pineapple?

Answer:

④ How many more people chose mushroom than pineapple?

Answer:

⑤ How many people preferred meat?

Answer:

⑥ How many one-topping pizzas were ordered in all?

Answer:

Joan asked her friends how many crackers they had for snack yesterday. Use the information below to complete the bar graph and answer the questions.

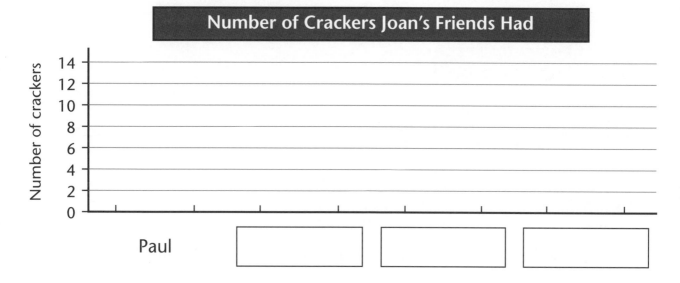

	Paul	Gary	Lesley	Irene
⑦ Number of crackers	⊪⊪ ⊪⊪	⊪⊪ I	⊪⊪ ⊪⊪ II	⊪⊪ III

Number of Crackers Joan's Friends Had

Number of crackers

14
12
10
8
6
4
2
0

Paul

⑧ How many crackers did Gary have?

Answer: _____

⑨ How many more crackers did Lesley have than Irene?

Answer: _____

⑩ Who had more crackers than Paul?

Answer: _____

⑪ How many crackers did the children have in all?

Answer: _____

CHALLENGE

Joan had more crackers than Gary but fewer than Irene. How many crackers did she have? Explain.

Answer: _____

Ann has 5 pencils. Help her measure the length of each pencil to the nearest centimetre.

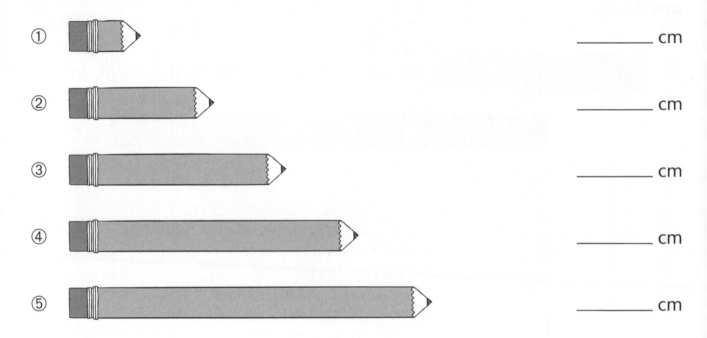

① _____ cm

② _____ cm

③ _____ cm

④ _____ cm

⑤ _____ cm

⑥ Look at the lengths of the pencils. What pattern do you notice?

Answer : _____

⑦ If Ann got 2 more pencils that followed the pattern, what would their lengths be?

Answer : _____

⑧ This is Ann's pencil box. What is its perimeter and area?

1cm

1cm

Answer : _____

Look at Ann's birthday gifts. Then check ✓ the side of each scale that would tip down.

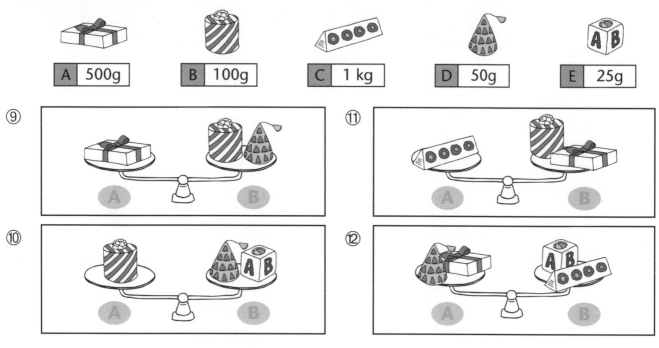

| A | 500g | | B | 100g | | C | 1 kg | | D | 50g | | E | 25g |

⑨
⑪
⑩
⑫

Look at Ann's birthday gifts again and answer the questions.

⑬　What is the shape of gift B? How many faces does it have?

Answer : _____

⑭　What is the shape of gift C? How many faces does it have?

Answer : _____

⑮　What is the shape of gift E? How many faces does it have?

Answer : _____

⑯　John says, 'The gift I bought for Ann can roll and its two ends are flat.' Which gift did John buy for Ann?

Answer : _____

⑰　Katie says, 'The gift I bought for Ann cannot roll and it has 5 faces.' Which gift did Katie buy for Ann?

Answer : _____

Use the pictograph to answer the questions.

Capacity of Containers	
Jug	🍵 🍵 🍵 🍵 🍵 🍵
Bottle	🍵 🍵 🍵
Glass	🍵
Vase	🍵 🍵 🍵 🍵 🍵 🍵 🍵 🍵

Each 🍵 holds 500 mL

⑱ What is the capacity of a jug?

Answer : _____

⑲ What is the capacity of a vase?

Answer : _____

⑳ How many millilitres are there in a litre?

Answer : _____

㉑ Which container has a capacity of less than 1 L?

Answer : _____

㉒ How many times is the capacity of a jug more than that of a bottle?

Answer : _____

㉓ How many bottles are needed to fill 3 L of juice?

Answer : _____

㉔ Which hold more, 2 bottles or 5 glasses?

Answer : _____

㉕ 2 jugs can fill a bucket. What is the capacity of a bucket?

Answer : _____

㉖ 4 bowls can fill a vase. What is the capacity of a bowl?

Answer : _____

Use the information below to complete the bar graph and answer the questions.

	Joan	Jane	Katie	George	David
Number of glasses of water	50	45	60	55	40

㉗

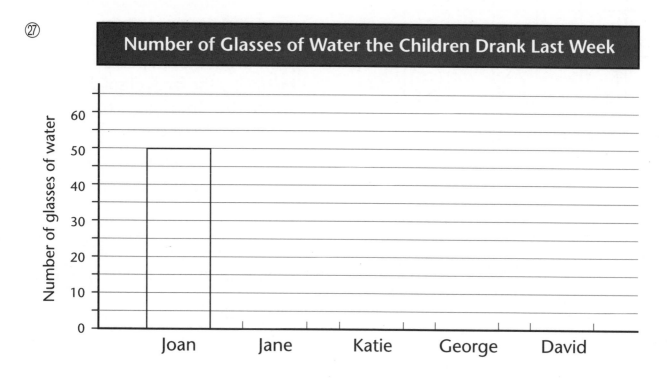

㉘ How many more glasses of water did George drink than David?

Answer : _____

㉙ If 6 glasses of water can fill a bottle, how many bottles of water did Katie drink?

Answer : _____

㉚ How many glasses of water did the children drink in all?

Answer : _____

㉛ What fraction of the total number of glasses of water did Joan drink?

Answer : _____

Look at the grid and answer the questions.

㉜ How many triangles are there?

Answer :

㉝ Which shape is 2 blocks up and 1 block to the left of the shaded triangle?

Answer :

㉞ Which shape is 1 block up and 2 blocks to the right of the shaded rectangle?

Answer :

㉟ How do you move from the shaded triangle to another triangle which is the farthest?

Answer :

㊱ How do you move from the shaded circle to another circle which is the closest?

Answer :

㊲ Joan drew the shapes on the grid by tracing the faces of solids. Which solid did Joan use to trace a rectangle and a triangle?

Answer :

㊳ How should Joan move ▱ to its slid image?

Answer :

㊴ How should she move ▱ to its flipped image?

Answer :

㊵ How should she move ▱ to its $\frac{1}{4}$ anti-clockwise turned image?

Answer :

1. Addition and Subtraction

↦ Children learn to add or subtract 3-digit whole numbers.

↦ To do addition,

1st   align the numbers on the right-hand side.

2nd add numbers from right to left (starting with the ones place).

3rd   carry groups of 10 from one column to the next column.

Example

Align the numbers.	Add the ones; then carry 1 ten to the tens column.	Add the tens; then carry 1 hundred to the hundreds column.	Add the hundreds.
$$\begin{array}{r} 347 \\ +\ \ 59 \\ \hline \end{array}$$	$$\begin{array}{r} {\scriptstyle 1} \\ 347 \\ +\ \ 59 \\ \hline 6 \end{array}$$ $7 + 9 = 16$	$$\begin{array}{r} {\scriptstyle 1\ 1} \\ 347 \\ +\ \ 59 \\ \hline 06 \end{array}$$ $1 + 4 + 5 = 10$	$$\begin{array}{r} {\scriptstyle 1} \\ 347 \\ +\ \ 59 \\ \hline 406 \end{array}$$ $1 + 3 = 4$

$347 + 59 = 406$

↦ To do subtraction,

1st   align the numbers on the right-hand side.

2nd subtract the number from right to left (starting with the ones place).

3rd   if the number is too small to subtract, borrow 1 from the column on the left.

Example

Align the numbers.	Borrow 1 ten from the tens column; subtract the ones.	Borrow 1 hundred from the hundreds column; subtract the tens.	Subtract the hundreds.
$$\begin{array}{r} 412 \\ -\ \ 68 \\ \hline \end{array}$$	$$\begin{array}{r} {\scriptstyle 0\ 12} \\ 4\,\cancel{1}\,2 \\ -\ \ 68 \\ \hline 4 \end{array}$$ $12 - 8 = 4$	$$\begin{array}{r} {\scriptstyle 3\ 10} \\ 4\,\cancel{1}\,2 \\ -\ \ 68 \\ \hline 44 \end{array}$$ $10 - 6 = 4$	$$\begin{array}{r} {\scriptstyle 3} \\ \cancel{4}\,12 \\ -\ \ 68 \\ \hline 344 \end{array}$$

$412 - 68 = 344$

2. Multiplication

↦ Children should understand that multiplication is repeated addition and be familiar with multiplying 1-digit whole numbers.

They should know that:

a. the product of two even numbers is even.

Example $2 \times 8 = 16$

b. the product of an even number and an odd number is even.

Example $4 \times 7 = 28$

c. the product of two odd numbers is odd.

Example $3 \times 9 = 27$

d. the product of any number multiplied by 5 has 0 or 5 at the ones place.

Example $4 \times 5 = 20$

Parents' Guide

- Even if the order of multiplication changes, the product remains the same.

  Example $6 \times 7 = 7 \times 6 = 42$

- When multiplying a 2-digit number by a 1-digit number, first multiply the ones, and then multiply the tens. Remember to carry if necessary.

  Example

  Multiply the ones.

  ```
     1
     2 4
  x    3
  -------
       2
  ```

  $24 \times 3 = 72$

  Multiply the tens.

  ```
     1
     2 4
  x    3
  -------
     7 2
  ```

  $3 \times 2 + 1 = 7$

  ↳ Add the 1 carried over.

3. Division

- Children should understand that division is the opposite of multiplication. They can recall the multiplication facts to do division. To do division, they should multiply the divisor by a number to get a product closest to the dividend. They can take the following steps to do division.

1st Divide	2nd Multiply	3rd Subtract	4th Bring down

- When the dividend is smaller than the divisor, put 0 in the quotient.

  Example

  Divide the tens.

  ```
      1      ← 3 ÷ 3 = 1
  3 ) 3 2
      3
  ```

  $32 \div 3 = 10\ R2$

  Divide the ones.

  ```
      1 0    ← Dividend 2 is smaller than the
  3 ) 3 2      divisor 3. Put 0 in the quotient.
      3
      ---
        2
  ```

4. Mixed Operations

- When an expression involves several operations, it must be done in the following order:

  1st do multiplication and division from left to right.

  2nd do addition and subtraction from left to right.

  Example $30 - 5 \times 2 = 30 - 10$ ← First, do the multiplication (5×2).

  $= 20$ ← Then do the subtraction ($30 - 10$).

5. Measurement

- Children learn to use centimetres, metres or kilometres in measuring lengths and distances. They need to know how to calculate the perimeters and areas of 2-dimensional figures and write them out using appropriate units.
- When the dimensions of a figure are not in the same unit, children should change them to the same unit before doing any calculation.

  Example

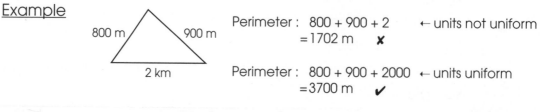

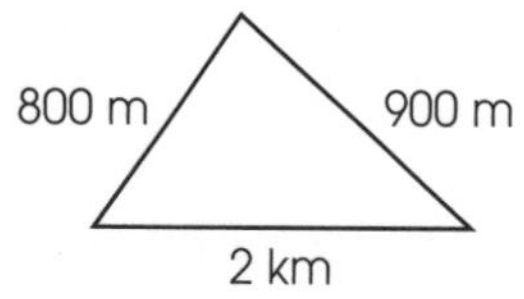

  Perimeter : $800 + 900 + 2$ ← units not uniform

  $= 1702$ m ✘

  Perimeter : $800 + 900 + 2000$ ← units uniform

  $= 3700$ m ✔

6. Time

✦ Children learn to estimate and measure the passage of time in five-minute intervals, and in days, weeks, months and years. They also learn how to tell and write time to the nearest minute using analog and digital clocks. Parents should give children daily practice to consolidate their knowledge of time.

Example

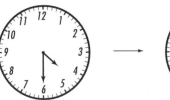 → 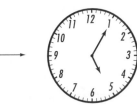   Duration : 35 minutes

7. Capacity

✦ In using standard units such as millilitre or litre to measure and record capacity of containers, children should know that the capacity of a 10-cm cube is 1 litre. Encourage children to make observations of different kinds of containers and let them recognize how much 1-litre is.

8. Shapes

✦ Children investigate the similarities and differences among a variety of prisms or pyramids using concrete materials and drawings. They also learn to name and describe prisms and pyramids by the shapes of their bases or ends. Parents should remind their children that prisms and pyramids are named by the shapes of the ends or bases.

Example

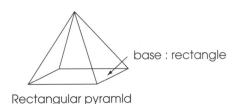

Rectangular pyramid

base : rectangle

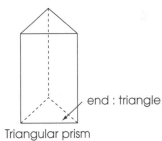

end : triangle

Triangular prism

9. Transformations

✦ Children learn to draw the lines of symmetry in 2-dimensional shapes and identify transformations, such as flips, slides and turns, using concrete materials and drawings. Rotations are limited to quarter turn, half turn and three-quarter turn only.

Example

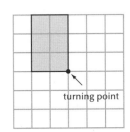

turning point

$\frac{3}{4}$ turn clockwise about the turning point ⟶

10. Coordinate Geometry

↔ Children learn to describe how to get from one point to another on a grid and the location of a point on a grid as an ordered pair of numbers. Through games and activities, children can learn this topic effectively.

Example

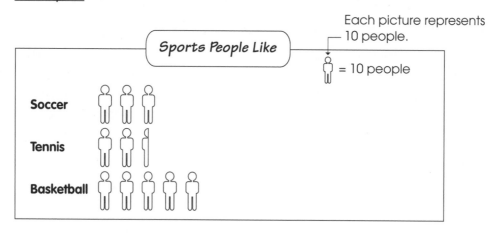

The ☆ is in the square (3 , 2).

           ↑   ↑
horizontal number   vertical number

11. Bar Graphs and Circle Graphs

↔ At this stage, children should know the quantity represented by each picture on a graph with many-to-one correspondence. They should also know how to use scales with multiples of 2,5 or 10, and interpret data and draw conclusions from the graphs. At this stage, children do not need to construct circle graphs, but they should be able to interpret them.

Examples

The most popular snack is chocolate.
A quarter of the students like lollipops.

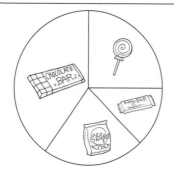

1 4-digit Numbers

1. 3268   2. 1986
3. 2371   4. 5734
5. 5734 ; 3268 ; 2371 ; 1986
6. 6541   7. 3068
8. 9523   9. 1274
10. Two thousand three hundred forty-one
11. Four thousand one hundred two
12. Seven thousand nine
13. 1200   14. 2050
15. 3400   16. 2025
17. 3   18. 9
19. 3
20. 9 big jars, 3 medium jars and 8 small jars.

2 Addition and Subtraction

1. Cedarbrae School
2. Brownsville School
3. 1050 – 426 = 624 ; 624
4. 1025 – 50 = 975 ; 975
5. 1330 + 50 = 1380 ; 1380
6. 1040 – 250 = 790 ; 790
7. 1245 – 319 = 926 ; 926
8. 582 + 1429 = 2011 ; 2011
9. 394 + 1066 = 1460 ; 1460
10. 1325 + 849 = 2174 ; 2174
11. 582 + 394 + 1325 = 2301 ; 2301
12. 1429 + 1066 + 849 = 3344 ; 3344
13. 3344 – 2301 = 1043 ; 1043
14. 3579   15. 3600
16. 4110   17. 4820
18. 3718   19. 3800
20. 1020   21. 3792
22. 4244   23. 3769
24. 892   25. 1855
26. 2778   27. 4002
28. 2439   29. 3021
30. 1978   31. 1144
32. Math is such fun!
33. 3590 + 2945 = 6535 ; 6535
34. 1782 + 2595 = 4377 ; 4377
35. 2595 – 1782 = 813 ; 813
36. 2945 – 1827 = 1118 ; 1118
37. 3590 + 260 = 3850 ; 3850
38. 1782 – 290 = 1492 ; 1492

3 Multiplication

1a. 3 ; 6 ; 9 ; 12 ; 15 ; 18
 b. 6   c. 6 ; 18
2a. 4 ; 8 ; 12 ; 16 ; 20 ; 24 ; 28
 b. 7   c. 7 ; 28
3a. 8 ; 16 ; 24 ; 32 ; 40 ; 48
 b. 6   c. 6 ; 48
4a. 7 ; 14 ; 21 ; 28 ; 35
 b. 5   c. 5 ; 35
5a. 2 ; 4 ; 6 ; 8 ; 10 ; 12 ; 14 ; 16
 b. 8   c. 8 ; 16
 6. B ; D ; 18   7. B ; C ; 20
 8. A ; D ; 28   9. B ; D ; 27
10. A ; B ; 12   11. B ; C ; 24
12a. 8 ; 64   b. 2 ; 16
13a. 2 ; 18   b. 5 ; 45
14a. 3 ; 18   b. 6 ; 36
15a. 4 ; 12   b. 3 ; 9
16a. 4 ; 28   b. 2 ; 14
17. 3 x 6 = 18 ; 18
18. 4 x 8 = 32 ; 32
19. 5 x 5 = 25 ; 25
20. 7 x 8 = 56 ; 56
21. 5 x 9 = 45 ; 45

4 Division

1a. 3   b. 3   2a. 2   b. 2
3a. 4   b. 4   4a. 7   b. 7
5a. 3   b. 3   6a. 3   b. 3
 7. 9
8.

3

9.

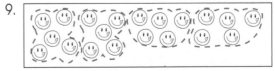

5

10.

7

11.

4

12.

4 ; 4

13.

28 ; 7 ; 7

14.

30 ; 6 ; 6

15.

40 ; 5 ; 5

16. 3 ; 3   17. 24 ; 6 ; 6

18. 26 ; 8 ; 2 ; 8 ; 2

19. 23 ; 4 ; 3 ; 4 ; 3

5 More about Multiplication and Division

1a. 3 ; 8   b. 3 ; 24 ; 24
2a. 4 ; 7   b. 4 ; 28 ; 28
3a. 20   b. 20 ; 4 ; 4
4a. 18   b. 18 ; 2 ; 2
5. 48 ÷ 8 = 6 ; 6
6. 3 x 9 = 27 ; 27
7. 8 x 3 = 24 ; 24
8. 36 ÷ 4 = 9 ; 9
9. 6 x 7 = 42 ; 42
10. 25 ÷ 5 = 5 ; 5
11. 3 x 6 = 18 ; 18

Midway Review

1. 1171 ; 1172 ; 1174
2. 2788 ; 2888 ; 3088
3. 8214 ; 6214 ; 4214
4. 4014 ; 4010 ; 4006
5. 3   6. 3947
7. 5068   8. 8373
9. 2   10. 9263
11. 7483
12. Eight thousand three hundred seventy-three
13. Eight hundred ninety
14.

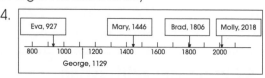

15. 927 + 2018 = 2945 ; 2945
16. 2018 – 927 = 1091 ; 1091
17. 1806 + 1446 = 3252 ; 3252
18. 1806 – 1446 = 360 ; 360
19. 1806 + 1129 = 2935 ; 2935
20. 927 + 2018 + 1446 = 4391 ; 4391
21a. 6 ; 18 ; 18   b. 24 ; 8 ; 8
22a. 5 ; 35 ; 35   b. 28 ; 4 ; 4
23a. 3 ; 27 ; 27   b. 18 ; 2 ; 2
24a. 12   b. 12
  c. 4   d. 6
25a. 18   b. 18
  c. 9   d. 3
26a. 24   b. 24
  c. 3   d. 4
27. 8 ; 4 ; 4   28. 9 ; 54 ; 54
29. 63 ; 9 ; 9   30. 4 ; 36 ; 36

6 Measurement

1.   2.
3. metre   4. hour
5. minute   6. 60
7. 24   8. 15
9. 44   10. 24
11. the flour   12. the cocoa
13. the sugar

14a.

b.

15. 1 hour 30 minutes

16a. 26   b. 22

17. the kitchen

7 Money

1a.

b.

2a.

b.

3a.

b.

4a.

b.

5a.

b.

6a. 68   b. 33
7a. 73   b. 26
8a. 69   b. 6
9a. 78   b. 55
10a. 97   b. 12
11a. 84   b. 30

12.

13.

14.

15.

16.

17.

18a. 16 + 16 = 32 ; 32
  b. 50 – 32 = 18 ; 18
19a. 37 + 37 = 74 ; 74
  b. 80 – 74 = 6 ; 6
20a. 18 + 18 + 18 = 54 ; 54
  b. 100 – 54 = 46 ; 46
21a. 29 + 29 + 29 = 87 ; 87
  b. 100 – 87 = 13 ; 13

8 Fractions and Decimals

1 – 10. (Suggested answers)

1.    2.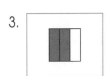

3.   4.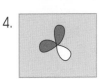

5.   6.

7.   8.

9.

10.

11. $\frac{3}{8}$ 12. $\frac{2}{5}$

13. $\frac{3}{6}$ 14. $\frac{2}{3}$

15. $\frac{1}{2}$ 16. $\frac{3}{4}$

17a.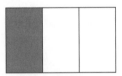

b.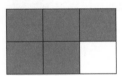

c.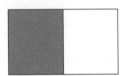

d. smaller ; greater

18a.   b.

c.

d. smaller ; greater

19. 7

20. $\frac{5}{7}$ 21. $\frac{3}{7}$

22. $\frac{4}{7}$ 23. $\frac{4}{7}$

24. $\frac{2}{7}$ 25. $\frac{1}{7}$

26. 0.3   27. 0.5

28. 0.8   29. 0.8

30. 0.7   31. 0.4

32. 0.5   33. 0.4

34 – 36. (Suggested answers)

34.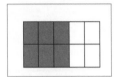

35.

36.

37. four   38. seven
39. eight   40. 2.35
41. 2.61   42. less
43. smaller   44. 3.09
45. 3.25   46. less
47. smaller   48. 0.75
49. 2.50   50. 1.75
51. less   52. more
53. smaller   54. greater

9 Graphs

1. Number of Heads Each Child Got
2. 4   3. 6
4. 3   5. 5
6. Gerrie   7. Iris
8. 2   9. 3
10. Sales of Doughnuts in Doug's Doughnut Shop Yesterday

11. Bar graph
12. 30
13. 50
14. Jellied
15. Sour dough
16. Honey
17. 240
18. 9 ; 6 ; 7 ; 5
19. Swimming
20. Hiking
21. 27
22.

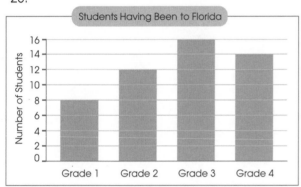

Favourite Summer Activities in Mrs Feler's Class

23.

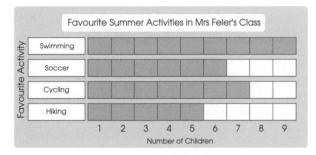

24. Students Having Been to Florida
25. 3
26. 1
27. 14
28. 5
29. 50

10 Probability

1. No
2. 4
3. 5
4. 1
5. 3
6. No
7. 4
8. 5
9. 1
10. B
11. A
12. C
13. C
14. B
15. D
16. A

Final Review

1. 67
2. 29
3. 49
4. 32
5a. 100 − 67 = 33 ; 33

   b.

6a. 100 − 49 − 32 = 19 ; 19

   b.

7a. 100 − 29 − 29 = 42 ; 42

   b.

8a.

b. 34

9a.

b. 38

10a. 13
    b. 9
11. B
12. A
13. 18
14. 5
15. 10
16. 2
17. Time for Homework Yesterday
18. Pictograph
19. 5
20. 13
21. 2
22.

Time for Homework Yesterday

less than half an hour	half an hour	one hour	one and a half hours	two hours

Time Spent

23. $\frac{2}{10}$; 0.2
24. $\frac{6}{10}$; 0.6
25. $\frac{5}{10}$; 0.5
26. $\frac{9}{10}$; 0.9
27. No
28. Red
29. White
30. Yes

31. No
32. Red
33. 11
34. $\frac{4}{11}$

35. $\frac{3}{11}$

36a.   b.

37 (Suggested answers)

a.

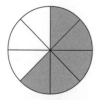

b.

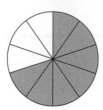

38. 4 ; 11 ; 7 ; 14
39. 7
40. 36
41. 92

1 Introducing Multiplication

1. 8 ; 8 ; 8
2. 12 , 15 ; 15 ; 15
3. 15 , 20 , 25 , 30 , 35 ; 35 ; 35
4. 12 , 16 , 20 , 24 ; 24 ; 24
5. 2 , 2 , 2 , 2 ; 5 ; 10
6. 4 , 4 , 3 ; 12
7. 5 , 5 , 3 ; 15
8. 6 ; 2 ; 12
9. 5 , 20 ; 5 , 20
10. 3 , 18 ; 3 , 18

11. 2 , 14 ; 2 , 14
12. 8 , 24 ; 8 , 24

13. 2 , 2 , 2 , 2 , 2 ; 6 ; 12
14. 3 , 3 , 3 , 3 ; 5 ; 15
15. 4 , 4 , 4 , 4 ; 5 ; 20
16. 5 , 5 , 3 ; 15
17. 5 ; 5 ; 5 , 45
18. 7 ; 7 ; 7 , 56
19. 4 ; 4 ; 4 , 20
20. 6 ; 6 ; 6 , 18
21. B   22. F   23. D   24. I
25. A   26. G   27. E   28. H
29. C   30. 5 ; 3 ; 5 , 3 ; 5 , 3 ; 15 ; 15

Just for Fun

1. I + II + III = IIIIII   or
2. IIIII − II − I = II

2 Multiplying by 2 or 5

1. 1 ; 1 ; 2   2. 2 ; 2 ; 4   3. 3 ; 3 ; 6
4. 4 ; 8   5. 5 ; 10   6. 6 ; 12
7. 7 ; 14   8. 8 ; 16   9. 9 ; 18
10. 2 , 4 , 6 , 8 , 10 , 12 , 14 , 16 , 18
11. 1 ; 1 ; 5   12. 2 ; 2 ; 10   13. 3 ; 3 ; 15
14. 4 ; 4 ; 20   15. 5 ; 5 ; 25   16. 6 ; 6 ; 30
17. 7 ; 7 ; 35   18. 8 ; 8 ; 40   19. 9 ; 9 ; 45
20. 5 , 10 , 15 , 20 , 25 , 30 , 35 , 40 , 45
21. 16   22. 20   23. 35   24. 10
25. 15   26. 12   27. 25   28. 4
29. 8   30. 40   31. 6   32. 10
33. 2   34. 45   35. 30   36. 18
37. 5   38. 14   39. 10   40. 10
41. 6   42. 18   43. 16   44. 25
45. 15   46. 40   47. 8   48. 12
49. 4   50. 14   51. 35   52. 20
53. 5   54. 18   55. 30   56. 2
57. 4 , 5 ; 20 ; 20   58. 6 , 2 ; 12 ; 12
     5   2
   x 4   x 6
   ────   ────
    2 0   1 2
59. 4 , 2 ; 8 ; 8   60. 3 , 5 ; 15 ; 15
     2   5
   x 4   x 3
   ────   ────
     8   1 5

Just for Fun

9 ; 2 ; 5 ; 4 ; 6 ; 1 ; 7 ; 3 ; 8

3 Multiplying by 3 or 4

2. 2 ; 2 ; 6   3. 3 ; 3 ; 9

---

4. 4 ; 4 ; 12   5. 5 ; 5 ; 15

6. 6 ; 6 ; 18   7. 7 ; 7 ; 21

8. 8 ; 8 ; 24

9. 3 ; 6 ; 9 ; 12 ; 15 ; 18 ; 21 ; 24 ; 27
10. 4   11. 8 ; 8
12. 12 ; 3 ; 12   13. 16 ; 4 ; 16
14. 20 ; 5 ; 20   15. 24 ; 6 ; 24
16. 28 ; 7 ; 28   17. 32 ; 8 ; 32
18. 36 ; 9 ; 36
19.

(number line from 0 to 40 marked at 0, 5, 10, 15, 20, 25, 30, 35, 40)

8 ; 12 ; 16 ; 20 ; 24 ; 28 ; 32 ; 36 ; 40

20. 15   21. 28   22. 16   23. 9
24. 6   25. 12.   26. 24   27. 32
28. 21   29. 4   30. 12   31. 18
32. 24   33. 36   34. 20   35. 27
36. 3   37. 8   38. 20   39. 24
40. 27   41. 21   42. 9   43. 32
44. 24   45. 36   46. 18   47. 28
48. 16   49. 15   50. 12   51. 3
52. 6   53. 4   54. 12   55. 8
56. 5 , 4 ; 20 ; 20   57. 4 , 3 ; 12 ; 12
     4   3
   x 5   x 4
   ────   ────
    2 0   1 2
58. 7 , 4 ; 28 ; 28   59. 8 , 3 ; 24 ; 24
     4   3
   x 7   x 8
   ────   ────
    2 8   2 4

Just for Fun

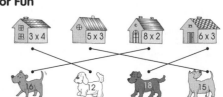

4 Multiplying by 6 or 7

1. 1 ; 1 ; 6   2. 2 ; 2 ; 12   3. 3 ; 3 ; 18
4. 4 ; 24   5. 5 ; 30   6. 6 ; 36
7. 7 ; 42   8. 8 ; 48   9. 9 ; 54
10. 6 ; 12 ; 18 ; 24 ; 30 ; 36 ; 42 ; 48 ; 54
11. 7   12. 14 ; 14   13. 21 ; 3 ; 21
14. 28 ; 4 ; 28   15. 35 ; 5 ; 35   16. 42 ; 6 ; 42
17. 49 ; 7 ; 49   18. 56 ; 8 ; 56   19. 63 ; 9 ; 63
20.

→	7	14	20	26	40	58
	12	21	28	34	56	63	→
	19	27	35	42	49	54

21. 24   22. 35   23. 21

24. 18	25. 36	26. 56	27. 14
28. 48	29. 54	30. 28	31. 7
32. 30	33. 12	34. 42	35. 49
36. 42	37. 63	38. 6	39. 21
40. 30	41. 18	42. 54	43. 14
44. 35	45. 15	46. 20	47. 6
48. 7	49. 24	50. 63	51. 36
52. 48	53. 49	54. 6	55. 56
56. 42	57. 12	58. 28	59. 42

60. 8 x 6 ; 48 ; 48   61. 5 x 7 ; 35 ; 35
62. 4 x 6 ; 24 ; 24   63. 6 x 7 ; 42 ; 42

Just for Fun

1. –, –   2. –, +   3. +, –   4. +, +

5 Multiplication Facts to 49

1a. 4 ; 8   b. 2 ; 8

c. 4 ; 2 ; 8
2a. 5 ; 15

b. 3 ; 15

c. 5 ; 3 ; 15
3a. 3 ; 12   b. 4 ; 12

c. 3 ; 4 ; 12
4. 10 ; 10 ; 5   5. 18 ; 18 ; 6   6. 28 ; 28 ; 4
7. 14 ; 14 ; 7   8. 30 ; 30 ; 6, 5   9. 20 ; 20 ; 4 ; 5
10. 7 ; 21   11. 4 ; 24   12. 6 ; 12
13. 5 ; 35   14. 6 ; 24   15. 9 ; 18
16. F   17. T   18. T   19. T
20. T   21. F   22. T   23. T
24a. 9 ; 9 ; 18   b. 6 ; 6 ; 18

c. 3 ; 3 ; 18   d. 9 ; 6 ; 3 ; 18

25a. 8 ; 8 ; 24   b. 6 ; 6 ; 24

c. 4 ; 4 ; 24   d. 8 ; 6 ; 4 ; 24

26. 7   27. 6   28. 5   29. 3
30. 9

Just for Fun

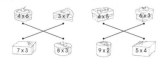

6 Multiplying by 8, 9, 0 or 1

1. 8 ; 8 ; 8 ; 8   2. 8 ; 8 ; 0 ; 0
3. 8 ; 8 ; 64 ; 64   4. 9 ; 9 ; 72 ; 72
5. 1 ; 8   6. 2 ; 16   7. 3 ; 24   8. 4 ; 32
9. 5 ; 40   10. 6 ; 48   11. 7 ; 56
12. 8 ; 16 ; 24 ; 32 ; 40 ; 48 ; 56 ; 64 ; 72
13. 1 ; 9   14. 2 ; 18   15. 3 ; 27   16. 4 ; 36
17. 5 ; 45   18. 6 ; 54   19. 7 ; 63   20. 8 ; 72
21. 81

22. 4	23. 0	24. 0	25. 3
26. 24	27. 36	28. 64	29. 18
30. 81	31. 16	32. 54	33. 72
34. 0	35. 8	36. 0	37. 7
38. 5	39. 27	40. 32	41. 0
42. 45	43. 0	44. 6	45. 56

46. 6 X 9 ; 54 ; 54   47. 9 X 0 ; 0 ; 0

$$\begin{array}{r} 9 \\ \times\ 6 \\ \hline 5\ 4 \end{array}\qquad\begin{array}{r} 0 \\ \times\ 9 \\ \hline 0 \end{array}$$

48. 7 x 1 ; 7 ; 7   49. 3 x 8 ; 24 ; 24

$$\begin{array}{r} 1 \\ \times\ 7 \\ \hline 7 \end{array}\qquad\begin{array}{r} 8 \\ \times\ 3 \\ \hline 2\ 4 \end{array}$$

Just for fun

7 More Multiplying

1. 30   2. 50   3. 40   4. 70
5. 3   6. 0   7. 60   8. 10
9. 90   10. 80   11. 56   12. 27
13. 42   14. 10
15.

	1	2	3	4	5	6	7	8	9	10
1	1	2	3	4	5	6	7	8	9	10
2	2	4	6	8	10	12	14	16	18	20
3	3	6	9	12	15	18	21	24	27	30
4	4	8	12	16	20	24	28	32	36	40
5	5	10	15	20	25	30	35	40	45	50
6	6	12	18	24	30	36	42	48	54	60
7	7	14	21	28	35	42	49	56	63	70
8	8	16	24	32	40	48	56	64	72	80
9	9	18	27	36	45	54	63	72	81	90
10	10	20	30	40	50	60	70	80	90	100

16. B ; E   17. A ; C   18. D ; F
19. 4 , 9 ; 36 ; 9 , 4 , 36
20. 4 , 8 ; 32 ; 8 , 4 , 32

21. 42	22. 27	23. 40
24. 0	25. 9	26. 70
27. 45	28. 18	29. 72
30. 14	31. 0	32. 18
33. 90	34. 28	35. 3 ; 21
36. 1 ; 8	37. 3 ; 6	38. 0 ; 0
39. 10 ; 8	40. 10 ; 20	

41. 10 X 0 ; 0 ; 0   42. 5 x 6 ; 30 ; 30
43. 8 x 4 ; 32 ; 32   44. 7 x 6 ; 42 ; 42
45. 4 x 9 ; 36 ; 36   46. 7 x 3 ; 21 ; 21

Just for Fun

1. 2 , 2 ; 2 , 2   2. 1 , 2 , 3 ; 1 , 2 , 3

8   Introducing Division

2. 3

3. 4   4. 9

5. 7   6. 4

7. 6

8. 5

9. 6

10. 4

11. 8

12. 5 ; 2

13. 8   14. 6   15. 4 ; 4
16. 3 ; 3 ; 3   17. 3 ; 3 ; 3   18. 6 ; 6 ; 6
19. 3 ; 3   20. 12 ; 12 , 4 ; 3 ; 3
21. 18 ; 18 , 3 ; 6 ; 6   22. 15 ; 15 , 5 ; 3 ; 3
23. 15 ; 15 , 3 ; 5 ; 5   24. 10 ; 10 , 5 ; 2 ; 2

Just for Fun

1. 6 ; 24 ; 0   2. 9 ; 45 ; 45

Midway Review

1. 2 , 4 , 12 , 14   2. 15 , 18 , 21 , 27
3. 25 , 30 , 40 , 45   4. 18 , 24 , 42 , 48
5. 21 , 28 , 49 , 56   6. 4 , 16 , 20 , 28
7. 18 , 54 , 63 , 72   8. 24 , 32 , 64 , 72
9. 5   10. 1
11. 0   12. 2 ; 4 ; 6 ; 8
13. 56   14. 0   15. 50   16. 30
17. 9   18. 14   19. 24   20. 12
21. 30   22. 8   23. 35   24. 18
25. 24   26. 45   27. 18   28. 28
29. 10   30. 21   31. 27   32. 0

33. 20   34. 12   35. 63   36. 7
37. 32   38. 18   39. 6   40. 40
41. 48   42. 36   43. 54
44. 1   45. 0   46. 0   47. 35
48. 40   49. 54   50. 4 ; 32   51. 4 ; 36
52. 0 ; 0   53. 10 ; 6   54. 3 ; 6   55. 6 ; 42
56. B   57. D   58. D   59. A
60. 8 ; 8 , 4 ; 2 ; 2   61. 12 ; 12 , 3 ; 4 ; 4
62. 6 ÷ 3 ; 2 ; 2   63. 6 x 4 ; 24 ; 24
64. 5 x 8 ; 40 ; 40   65. 3 x 7 ; 21 ; 21
66. 4

9   Multiplication and Division Fact Families

1. 3 ; 3   2. 5 ; 5   3. 3 ; 3   4. 4 ; 4
5. 5 ; 5   6. 2 ; 2   7. 4 ; 4
8. 15 ; 5 , 3 ; 15 ; 15 , 3 ; 5 ; 15 , 5 ; 3
9. 16 ; 8 , 2 ; 16 ; 16 , 2 ; 8 ; 16 , 8 ; 2
10. 3 , 7 ; 21 ; 7 , 3 ; 21 ; 21 , 3 ; 7 ; 21 , 7 ; 3
11. 3 , 6 ; 18 ; 6 , 3 ; 18 ; 18 , 3 ; 6 ; 18 , 6 ; 3
12. 4 , 6 ; 24 ; 6 , 4 ; 24 ; 24 , 6 ; 4 ; 24 , 4 ; 6
13. 4 , 5 ; 20 ; 5 , 4 ; 20 ; 20 , 5 ; 4 ; 20 , 4 ; 5
14. 6 ; 3   15. 4 ; 9   16. 8 ; 6
17. 7 ; 4   18. 3 ; 8   19. 7 ; 5
20. 54 ; 9   21. 40 ; 5   22. 32 ; 4
23. 27 ; 9   24. 42 ; 6   25. 45 ; 9
26. 4 ; 4   27. 6 ; 6   28. 7 ; 7
29. 9 ; 9   30. 3 ; 3   31. 6 ; 6
32. 9 ; 9 ; 81   33. 8 ; 8   34. 6 ; 6 ; 36
35. 7 , 8 ; 56 ; 8 , 7 ; 56 ; 56 , 8 ; 7 ; 56 , 7 ; 8
36. 8 , 9 ; 72 ; 9 , 8 ; 72 ; 72 , 9 ; 8 ; 72 , 8 ; 9
37.- 40. (Suggested answers)
37. 6 , 2 ; 12 ; 12 , 2 ; 6   38. 8 , 5 ; 40 ; 40 , 5 ; 8
39. 5 , 6 ; 30 ; 30 , 6 ; 5   40. 9 , 5 ; 45 ; 45 , 5 ; 9

Just for Fun

10   Dividing by 1, 2 or 3

2. 8 ; 4

3. 4 ; 4   4. 6 ; 3

5. 12 ; 4   6. 8 ; 4

7. 5 ; 5   8. 12 ; 4

9. 5 ; 5 ; 5   10. 6 ; 6 ; 6
11. 9 ; 9 ; 9   12. 7 ; 7 ; 7
14. 7   15. 8   16. 4 ; 12   17. 6 ; 6
18. 9 ; 18   19. 7 ; 7   20. 3 ; 6   21. 9 ; 27
22. 8   23. 8   24. 2   25. 10
26. 4   27. 3   28. 6   29. 4

30. 2 31. 9 32. 6 33. 2
34. 1 35. 3 36. 5 37. 1
38. 5 39. 5

40.
```
     4
3 | 12
    12
```
41.
```
     4
2 | 8
    8
```
42.
```
    4
1 | 4
    4
```
43.
```
     7
2 | 14
    14
```

44.
```
    3
3 | 9
    9
```
45.
```
     7
3 | 21
    21
```
46.
```
     9
3 | 27
    27
```
47.
```
    8
1 | 8
    8
```

48.
```
     8
2 | 16
    16
```
49.
```
    3
1 | 3
    3
```
50.
```
    3
2 | 6
    6
```
51.
```
    2
3 | 6
    6
```

52. 24 , 3 ; 8 ; 8
```
     8
3 | 24
    24
```
53. 16 , 2 ; 8 ; 8
```
     8
2 | 16
    16
```

54. 6 , 1 ; 6 ; 6
```
    6
1 | 6
    6
```
55. 12 , 2 ; 6 ; 6
```
     6
2 | 12
    12
```

Just for Fun
16

11 Dividing by 4 or 5

2. 20 ; 4
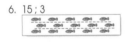

3. 30 ; 6

4. 16 ; 4

5. 24 ; 6

6. 15 ; 3

7. 12 ; 3

8.
×	1	2	3	4	5	6	7	8	9
4	4	8	12	16	20	24	28	32	36
5	5	10	15	20	25	30	35	40	45

9. 2   10. 4   11. 3
12. 8   13. 6   14. 4
15. 8   16. 7   17. 9
18. 5   19. 9   20. 7
21. 6   22. 1   23. 3
24. 1   25. 5   26. 2
27.
```
     4
4 | 16
    16
```
28.
```
     6
5 | 30
    30
```
29.
```
     5
4 | 20
    20
```
30.
```
     9
5 | 45
    45
```
31.
```
     8
4 | 32
    32
```
32.
```
     5
5 | 25
    25
```
33.
```
     9
4 | 36
    36
```
34.
```
     8
5 | 40
    40
```
35.
```
     6
4 | 24
    24
```

36.

37. 8   38. 8   39. 35
40. 5   41. 20   42. 4
43. 32   44. 5   45. 15
46. 24   47. 25   48. 4
49. 5   50. 6 ; 24   51. 5
52. 30 , 5 ; 6 ; 6   53. 36 , 4 ; 9 ; 9
54. 28 , 4 ; 7 ; 7   55. 20 , 5 ; 4 ; 4

Just for Fun
1. – , + , –   2. – , + , –   3. – , + , + or + , – , –
4. + , – , +   5. + , + , –   6. + , + , +

12 Dividing by 6 or 7

2.
21 ; 3 ; 3 ; 21

3.
18 ; 3 ; 3 ; 18

4.
28 ; 4 ; 4 ; 28

5. 9 ; 9   6. 6 ; 6
7. 7 ; 7   8. 9 ; 6 x 9 = 54
9. 6 ; 7 x 6 = 42   10. 4 ; 6 x 4 = 24
11. 4 ; 7 x 4 = 28   12. 5 ; 6 x 5 = 30
13. 3 ; 7 x 3 = 21   14. 3 ; 6 x 3 = 18
15. 2 ; 7 x 2 = 14   16. 8 ; 6 x 8 = 48
17. 2   18. 5   19. 7
20. 1   21. 1   22. 8
23.
```
     6
6 | 36
    36
```
24.
```
     3
7 | 21
    21
```
25.
```
     7
7 | 49
    49
```
26.
```
     4
7 | 28
    28
```
27.
```
     9
6 | 54
    54
```
28.
```
     3
6 | 18
    18
```
29. ✓   30. ✗ ; 8
31. ✓   32. ✗ ; 6
33. ✓   34. ✗ ; 8
35. 30   36. 7   37. 48
38. 21   39. 6   40. 7
41. 6   42. 56   43. 7
44. 7   45. 30   46. 54
47. 7   48. 7   49. 7
50. 8   51. 3 ; 21   52. 6
53. 54 , 6 ; 9 ; 9; check: 6 x 9 = 54

54. 56 , 7 ; 8 ; 8; check: 7 x 8 = 56
55. 24 , 6 ; 4 ; 4; check: 6 x 4 = 24
56. 35 , 7 ; 5 ; 5; check: 7 x 5 = 35

Just for Fun

A ; E

13 Dividing by 8 or 9

1. 9 ; 3
2. 4 , 8 ; 8 , 4
3. 45 , 5 ; 9 ; 45 , 9 ; 5
4. 40 , 5 ; 8 ; 40 , 8 ; 5
5. 8 ; 8
6. 8 ; 8
7. 4 ; 4
8. 5 ; 5
9. 4 ; 4
10. 7 ; 7
11. 3 ; 3
12. 2 ; 2
13. 3 ; 3
14. 5 ; 5
15. 2 ; 2
16. 6 ; 6
17. 1 ; 1
18. 6 ; 6
19. 9 ; 9
20. 7 ; 7
21. 9 ; 9
22. 1 ; 1

23.
```
     2
8 ) 16
    16
```
24.
```
     9
8 ) 72
    72
```
25.
```
     4
9 ) 36
    36
```
26.
```
     6
9 ) 54
    54
```
27.
```
     5
9 ) 45
    45
```
28.
```
     8
8 ) 64
    64
```
29.
```
     7
8 ) 56
    56
```
30.
```
     9
9 ) 81
    81
```
31.
```
     4
8 ) 32
    32
```

32. E ; F ; G ; I
33. A ; D ; H ; L
34. B ; C ; J ; K
35. 54 , 9 ; 6 ; 6
36. 56 , 8 ; 7 ; 7
37. 45 , 9 ; 5 ; 5

Just for Fun

1. 96
2. 103
3. 1036
4. 601

14 Division with Remainders

2.  14 ; 4R2

3.  27 ; 3R3

4.  26 ; 5R1

5. 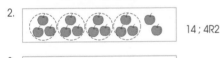 20 ; 3R2

6. 6 ; 1
7. 5 ; 5
8. 8R8
9. 3R2
10. 8R3
11. 5R2
12. 6R2
13. 5R1
14. 8R1
15. 5R6
16. 7R4
17. 7R1

18.
```
    2 R7
9 ) 25
    18
     7
```
19.
```
    6 R1
3 ) 19
    18
     1
```
20.
```
    9 R1
5 ) 46
    45
     1
```
21.
```
    9 R1
6 ) 55
    54
     1
```
22.
```
    7 R3
7 ) 52
    49
     3
```
23.
```
    9 R2
4 ) 38
    36
     2
```

24.
```
    9 R7
8 ) 79
    72
     7
```
25.
```
    6 R3
6 ) 39
    36
     3
```
26.
```
    6 R1
3 ) 19
    18
     1
```
27.
```
    5 R2
3 ) 17
    15
     2
```
28.
```
    3 R1
7 ) 22
    21
     1
```
29.
```
    9 R2
4 ) 38
    36
     2
```
30.
```
    6 R1
9 ) 55
    54
     1
```
31.
```
    7 R2
6 ) 44
    42
     2
```
32.
```
    8 R1
8 ) 65
    64
     1
```
33.
```
    5 R1
5 ) 26
    25
     1
```
34.
```
    9 R1
2 ) 19
    18
     1
```
35.
```
    9 R2
3 ) 29
    27
     2
```
36.
```
    8 R5
6 ) 53
    48
     5
```
37.
```
    3 R1
4 ) 13
    12
     1
```
38.
```
    7 R4
7 ) 53
    49
     4
```
39.
```
    4 R6
8 ) 38
    32
     6
```
40.
```
    5 R1
9 ) 46
    45
     1
```
41.
```
    8 R1
5 ) 41
    40
     1
```

42. cupboard
43. 20 ÷ 6 ; 3R2 ; 3 ; 2
44. 12 ÷ 5 ; 2R2 ; 2 ; 2
45. 89 ÷ 9 ; 9R8 ; 9 ; 8

Just for Fun

1. 50 , 53 , 58 , 80 , 83 , 85
2. 308 , 350 , 358 , 380 , 508 , 530 , 538 , 580
3. 803 , 805 , 830 , 835 , 850 , 853

15 More Dividing

1. 24 ; 24
2. 6R1 ; 6 x 3 = 18 ; 18 + 1 = 19
3. 6R3 ; 6 x 7 = 42 ; 42 + 3 = 45
4. 7R4 ; 7 x 5 = 35 ; 35 + 4 = 39
5. 8R3 ; 8 x 5 = 40 ; 40 + 3 = 43
6. 7R7 ; 7 x 9 = 63 ; 63 + 7 = 70
7. 6R1 ; 6 x 4 = 24 ; 24 + 1 = 25
8. 7R1 ; 7 x 2 = 14 ; 14 + 1 = 15

9.
```
    8 R1
9 ) 73
    72
     1
```
10.
```
    7
4 ) 28
    28
```
11.
```
    3
5 ) 15
    15
```
12.
```
    8 R2
3 ) 26
    24
     2
```
13.
```
    6 R3
6 ) 39
    36
     3
```
14.
```
    6
8 ) 48
    48
```
15.
```
    9
2 ) 18
    18
```
16.
```
    4 R1
7 ) 29
    28
     1
```
17.
```
    8 R2
4 ) 34
    32
     2
```

18.
```
   5R4
5 ) 29
    25
     4
```

19.
```
    6
3 ) 18
    18
```

20.
```
    4R4
9 ) 40
    36
     4
```

21.
```
    8
6 ) 48
    48
```

22.
```
    4R2
8 ) 34
    32
     2
```

23.
```
    5R1
2 ) 11
    10
     1
```

24.
```
    5
7 ) 35
    35
```

25.
```
    5R2
4 ) 22
    20
     2
```

26.
```
    9R2
5 ) 47
    45
     2
```

27. 18 ÷ 4 = 4R2 ⟶ 36 ÷ 6 = 6 ⟶ 27 ÷ 7 = 3R6 ⟶ 54 ÷ 9 = 6
⟶ 42 ÷ 6 = 7 ⟶ 13 ÷ 2 = 6R1 ⟶ 21 ÷ 3 = 7 ⟶ 35 ÷ 8 =
4R3 ⟶ 27 ÷ 3 = 9 ⟶ 45 ÷ 9 = 5

28. 24 ÷ 8 = 3
29. 46 ÷ 5 = 9R1 ✓
30. 30 ÷ 6 = 5
31. 56 ÷ 8 = 7
32. 27 ÷ 9 = 3
33. 26 ÷ 4 = 6R2 ✓
34. 38 ÷ 7 = 5R3 ✓

Just for Fun

1 + 4 = 5 ; 2 x 3 = 6

16 More Multiplying and Dividing

1.
```
    0
  x 8
    0
```

2.
```
    7
  x 6
   42
```

3.
```
    8
7 ) 56
    56
```

4.
```
    9
4 ) 36
    36
```

5.
```
    6
3 ) 18
    18
```

6.
```
    8
6 ) 48
    48
```

7.
```
    7
5 ) 35
    35
```

8.
```
    7
9 ) 63
    63
```

9.
```
    6
2 ) 12
    12
```

10.
```
    9
8 ) 72
    72
```

11.
```
    5
  x 2
   10
```

12.
```
    3
  x 0
    0
```

13.
```
   10
  x 5
   50
```

14.
```
    1
  x 9
    9
```

15a. 20   b. 4 , 5 ; 20   c. 20 ; 4   d. 20 ; 5
16a. 9 , 3 ; 27   b. 3 , 9 ; 27
c. 27 , 3 ; 9   d. 27 , 9 ; 3
17a. 3 , 4 ; 12   b. 4 , 3 ; 12
c. 12 , 3 ; 4   d. 12 , 4 ; 3
18a. 3 , 5 ; 15   b. 5 , 3 ; 15
c. 15 , 5 ; 3   d. 15 , 3 ; 5
19. C   20. D   21. A   22. E
23. B   24. H   25. F   26. I
27. G
28. 3 x 8 ; 24 ; 24   29. 12 ÷ 6 ; 2 ; 2
30. 4 x 8 ; 32 ; 32   31. 28 ÷ 5 ; 5R3 ; 3

Just for fun

1 + 7 = 8 ; 9 – 4 = 5 ; 2 x 3 = 6

Final Review

1. 20 , 30 , 35 , 40   2. 27 , 54 , 63 , 72
3. 14 , 10 , 8 , 6   4. 28 , 24 , 16 , 12

5. 72 , 48 , 32 , 24
6. 4   7. 9   8. 8   9. 28
10. 18   11. 35   12. 9   13. 8
14. 9   15. 24   16. 20   17. 20
18. 9   19. 8   20. 7   21. 24
22. 48   23. 15   24. 0   25. 7R2
26. 6R4   27. 8R1   28. 7R3

29.
```
    8
6 ) 48
    48
```

30.
```
    7
5 ) 35
    35
```

31.
```
    4
7 ) 28
    28
```

32.
```
    9
2 ) 18
    18
```

33.
```
    8
4 ) 32
    32
```

34.
```
    6
3 ) 18
    18
```

35.
```
    7
8 ) 56
    56
```

36.
```
    4
9 ) 36
    36
```

37.
```
    6
  x 7
   42
```

38.
```
    8
  x 2
   16
```

39.
```
    1
  x 5
    5
```

40.
```
    9
  x 9
   81
```

41.
```
    3
  x 9
   27
```

42.
```
    4
  x 9
   36
```

43.
```
    0
  x 7
    0
```

44.
```
    5
  x 6
   30
```

45.
```
    7
9 ) 63
    63
```

46.
```
    7
2 ) 14
    14
```

47.
```
    9
5 ) 45
    45
```

48.
```
    8
3 ) 24
    24
```

49.
```
    8R1
6 ) 49
    48
     1
```

50.
```
    8R1
4 ) 33
    32
     1
```

51.
```
    5R5
8 ) 45
    40
     5
```

52.
```
    8
7 ) 56
    56
```

53. 9 , 5 ; 45 ; 5 , 9 ; 45 ; 45 , 9 ; 5 ; 45 , 5 ; 9
54. 8 , 4 ; 32 ; 4 , 8 ; 32 ; 32 , 8 ; 4 ; 32 , 4 ; 8
55. 7 ; 7   56. 8 ; 8   57. 9 ; 9   58. 6 ; 6
59. 7 ; 7   60. 9 ; 9   61. 7 ; 7   62. 9 ; 9
63. 5 ; 5   64. 36   65. 2   66. 3
67. 4   68. 5   69. 7   70. 6
71. x   72. 2   73. 32   74. ÷
75. 0   76. 1   77. 10   78. 6
79. 4 ; 32   80. 2 ; 12   81. 0 ; 0   82. 6 ; 3
83. 4 ; 4   84. 0 ; 0   85. 20 ; 3   86. 8 ; 9
87. – 88. (Suggested answers)
87. 6 , 8 ; 48 ; 48 , 6 ; 8   88. 5 , 7 ; 35 ; 35 , 7 ; 5
89. 2 x 8 ; 16 ; 16   90. 9 x 4 ; 36 ; 36
91. 36 ÷ 6 ; 6 ; 6   92. 34 ÷ 4 ; 8R2 ; 8 ; 2

1 Multiples

1 - 5.

1	2	3	4	5	6	7	8	9	10
11	12	13	14	15	16	17	18	19	20
21	22	23	24	25	26	27	28	29	30
31	32	33	34	35	36	37	38	39	40
41	42	43	44	45	46	47	48	49	50
51	52	53	54	55	56	57	58	59	60
61	62	63	64	65	66	67	68	69	70
71	72	73	74	75	76	77	78	79	80
81	82	83	84	85	86	87	88	89	90
91	92	93	94	95	96	97	98	99	100

- Orange
- Yellow
- Orange + Yellow

6. 2
7. 2, 4
8. In columns
9. Diagonally
10. 40, 80
11. Even numbers
12. 3
13. 3, 9
14. 11
15. 33, 66, 99
16. 99
17. Yes
18. Diagonally

19 - 20.

1	2	3	4	5	6	7
8	9	10	11	12	13	14
15	16	17	18	19	20	21
22	23	24	25	26	27	28
29	30	31	32	33	34	35
36	37	38	39	40	41	42
43	44	45	46	47	48	49
50	51	52	53	54	55	56
57	58	59	60	61	62	63
64	65	66	67	68	69	70

21. In a column
22. Diagonally
23. 42
24. 10
25. 8, 16, 24, 32, 40
26. 6, 12, 18, 24, 30
27. 27, 36, 45
28. 35, 42, 49
29. 55, 66, 77
30. 78, 84, 90
31. 72, 80, 88
32. ✓
33.
34. ✓
35. ✓
36.
37.
38. ✓

Activity

1. 6, 8, 10, 12; 2
2. 21, 28, 35, 42; 7

2 Brackets

1. 13; 7
   7
2. 21 - 18 = 3
   3
3. 17 - 4
   13
4. 74 + 15
   89
5. 35 - 16
   19
6. 52 - 33
   19
7. 16 + 24
   40
8. 14 + 14
   28

9. 20
10. 7
11. 6
12. 21
13. 12
14. 12
15. 6, 2, 12
16. 10 + 9
    19
17. (16 + 4) + 23
    20 + 23 = 43
18. 1; 37
19. 5; 46

Activity

6, 4

3 Addition and Subtraction

1. 6424, 6000
2. 5994

$$\begin{array}{r} 3\,0\,0\,0 \\ 2\,0\,0\,0 \\ +\ 1\,0\,0\,0 \\ \hline 6\,0\,0\,0 \end{array}$$

3. 4895
4. 4630
5. 3865
6. 6041
7. 8784
8. 5595
9. 7936
10. 8931
11. 4099, 4000
12. 3918

$$\begin{array}{r} 6\,0\,0\,0 \\ -\ 2\,0\,0\,0 \\ \hline 4\,0\,0\,0 \end{array}$$

13. 3811
14. 1259
15. 2177
16. 279
17. 1149
18. 1456

Activity

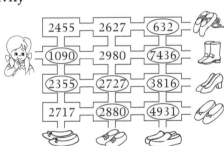

4 Multiplication

1. 21
2. 35
3. 24
4. 80
5. 18
6. 27
7. 64
8. 42
9. 72
10. 30
11. 32
12. 40
13. 6
14. 54
15. You are fantastic!
16. 46
17. 68
18. 93
19. 78
20. 129
21. 156
22. 168
23. 219
24. 26 x 3 = 78; 78

25. 27 x 4 = 108
108

```
    27
 x   4
   108
```

26. 95

```
    20
 x   5
   100
```

27. 196

```
    30
 x   7
   210
```

28. 234

```
    40
 x   6
   240
```

29. 336

```
    50
 x   7
   350
```

30. 265

```
    50
 x   5
   250
```

31. 6, 5 ,7 , 756

32. 225 x 7 = 1575
1575

```
   225
 x   7
  1575
```

33. 1176

```
   400
 x   3
  1200
```

34. 3654

```
   400
 x   9
  3600
```

35. 2440

```
   300
 x   8
  2400
```

36. 1635

```
   500
 x   3
  1500
```

37. 2456

```
   600
 x   4
  2400
```

38. 346 x 7 = 2422
2422

```
   346
 x   7
  2422
```

39. 225 x 5 = 1125
1125

```
   225
 x   5
  1125
```

40. 150 x 8 = 1200
1200

```
   150
 x   8
  1200
```

41. 165 x 4 = 660
660

```
   165
 x   4
   660
```

Activity

1. 168, 168, 168
2. 5148, 5148, 5148
3. No

5   Division

1. 67, 8, 8 r 3
2. 43, 7, 6 r 1
3. 32 ÷ 9 = 3 r 5
4. 58 ÷ 6 = 9 r 4

5.
```
      6 r 1
  6 ) 3 7
      3 6
       1
```

6.
```
      6 r 1
  4 ) 2 5
      2 4
       1
```

7.
```
      3 r 0
  8 ) 2 4
      2 4
       0
```

8.
```
      4 r 3
  9 ) 3 9
      3 6
       3
```

9.
```
       1 r 1
  10 ) 1 1
       1 0
        1
```

10.
```
      8 r 8
  9 ) 8 0
      7 2
       8
```

11.
```
      4 r 1
  2 ) 9
      8
      1
```

12.
```
      8 r 5
  8 ) 6 9
      6 4
       5
```

13.
```
      4 r 8
  9 ) 4 4
      3 6
       8
```

14.
```
      7 r 1
  6 ) 4 3
      4 2
       1
```

15. great
16. 21
17. 11, 2

18.
```
      2 1 r 0
  4 ) 8 4
      8
      4
      4
      0
```

19.
```
      1 1 r 2
  5 ) 5 7
      5
      7
      5
      2
```

20.
```
      3 3 r 0
  3 ) 9 9
      9
      9
      9
      0
```

21.
```
      1 1 r 2
  6 ) 6 8
      6
      8
      6
      2
```

22. 11 r 4
23. 34 r 1
24. 11 r 2
25. 21 r 1
26. 21 r 2
27. 11 r 1

28.
```
      1 5 r 0
  5 ) 7 5
      5
      2 5
      2 5
       0
```

29.
```
      1 7 r 1
  4 ) 6 9
      4
      2 9
      2 8
       1
```

30.
```
      2 3 r 2
  4 ) 9 4
      8
      1 4
      1 2
       2
```

31. 13 r 1
32. 27 r 2

33.
```
      1 0 r 3
  6 ) 6 3
      6
      3
      0
      3
```

34.
```
      2 0 r 2
  4 ) 8 2
      8
      2
      0
      2
```

35.
$$3 \overline{)61} \quad 20\,r\,1$$
$$6$$
$$1$$
$$0$$
$$1$$

36.
$$5 \overline{)54} \quad 10\,r\,4$$
$$5$$
$$4$$
$$0$$
$$4$$

37. 10 r 2   38. 20 r 1

39.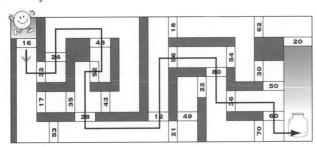

40.

41.

42.

Activity

6 Length

1. 18	2. 46	3. 35
4. 18 + 35 = 53	5. 27 + 35 = 62	6. 25 + 46 = 71
7. 2004	8. 400	9. 6008
10. 4	11. 1	12. 5, 9, 15, 11, 18, 11, 6
13. 27	14. 26	15. 9
16. 90	17. 34	18. 58
19. 43	20. 74	21. 20

Activity

1. Nancy   2. 63   3. 1700

7 Time

1.

2	9:00 a.m.	Cartoon Time	9 o' clock
4	11:50 a.m.	Music Video	10 minutes to 12
1	8:25 a.m.	Uncle Sam's Time	25 minutes past 8
7	8:55 p.m.	Toy Street	5 minutes to 9
5	4:45 p.m.	Games for Kids	15 minutes to 5
3	10:15 a.m.	Movie Time	15 minutes past 10
6	7:20 p.m.	Top Ten Songs	20 minutes past 7

2. 60   3. 55

4.   5.

6. 07:46:06   7. 04:09:38   8. 09:28:00
9. minutes   10. hours   11. seconds

Activity

1. Felix   2. Peter

8 Triangles

1-4 suggested answers

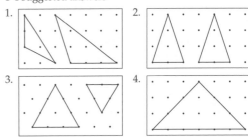

5. 6   6. 2

7.

8.    9.

Activity

1. 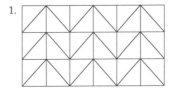   2.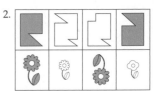

9 Perimeter

1. 60	2. 12
3. 12	4. 16
5. 16	6. 18
7. 30	8. 10 + 10 + 10 + 10 = 40

9. 7 + 3 + 7 + 3 = 20
10. 8 + 8 + 8 + 8 = 32
11. 4 x 2 = 8   12. 2 x (4 + 2) = 12

Activity

A. 18   B. 12   C. 14

10 Bar Graphs

1. Green	2. Red
3. Purple	4. Black
5. 15	6. 7
7. Yellow and Blue	8. 28

9.

The Children's Breakfast

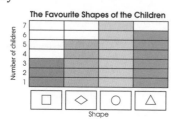

Number of children (vertical axis, 1–10)

Toast | Muffin | Cereal | Waffle
Breakfast

10. 7
11. Muffin
12. Waffle
13. 28

Activity

The Favourite Shapes of the Children

Number of children (vertical axis 1–7)

□ ◇ ○ △
Shape

11 5-digit Numbers

1. 10 000 + 2 000 + 300 + 60 + 0
   Twelve thousand three hundred sixty
2. 50 000 + 6 000 + 300 + 30 + 4
   Fifty-six thousand three hundred thirty-four
3. 23 275   4. 43 093
5. 99 999   6. 10 001
7. 79 998, 79 999, 80 000, 80 001, 80 002
8. 20 563, 20 653, 23 056, 25 063, 26 053
9. 3 000   10. 60
11. 40 000   12. 200

Activity

	58000	68000	78000	88000	98000
148000				87000	
238000	248000	258000	268000	86000	
348000				85000	
448000		64000	74000	84000	94000
548000				83000	

Midway Test

1. 4   2. 3   3. 5
4. 9   5. 6, 12, 18   6. 48, 56
7. 77, 88   8. 56, 63   9. 10, 2
10. 17, 33
11. 89 - 60   12. 56 - 18   13. 27 + 22
    29   38   49
14. 6322   15. 7390   16. 8903
17. 868   18. 1714   19. 1701

20. 3865   21. 3454   22. 333
23. 623   24. 2934   25. 1138

26.
```
    1 4 r 1
6 ) 8 5
    6
    2 5
    2 4
        1
```

27.
```
    1 2 r 5
6 ) 7 7
    6
    1 7
    1 2
        5
```

28.
```
    1 3 r 0
5 ) 6 5
    5
    1 5
    1 5
        0
```

29.
```
    3 2 r 1
3 ) 9 7
    9
    7
    6
    1
```

30.
```
    2 0 r 2
4 ) 8 2
    8
    2
    0
    2
```

31. 3150

32.
```
    1 9 r 1
5 ) 9 6
    5
    4 6
    4 5
        1
```

33. 540

34. 650   35. 1020   36. 1200
37. 900 + 450 = 1350   38. 900 + 650 = 1550
39. 450 + 500 = 950
40. 05:50:12   41. 09:05:57   42. 03:35:07
43.   44.

45. (48 cm + 39 cm) x 2   46. 26 m x 4
    174   104
47. (6 cm + 5 cm) x 2   48. 4 m x 4
    22   16
49. 4   50. 4   51. 2
52. 2
53.

The Favourite Sports

Number of students (vertical axis 1–9)

Basketball | Baseball | Soccer | Hockey

54. 7   55. 4   56. 24
57. Nancy   58. 2   59. 1
60. 17   61. 6 000   62. 50 000
63. 200   64. 50
65. Twenty thousand six hundred fifty-four
66. Thirty-seven thousand forty-nine

12 Factors

1. a. 2   b. 6
2. a. 4   b. 6   c. 12
   d. 1, 2, 3, 4, 6, 12
3. a. 10   b. 5   c. 20
   d. 1, 2, 4, 5, 10, 20
4 - 14.

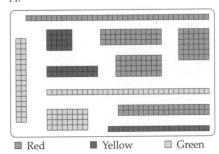

   ■ Red   ■ Yellow   □ Green

15. 2 x 10 = 4 x 5   16. 2 x 16 = 4 x 8
17. 2 x 18 = 3 x 12 = 4 x 9 = 6 x 6
18. 1, 2, 4, 5, 10, 20   19. 1, 2, 4, 8, 16, 32
20. 1, 2, 3, 4, 6, 9, 12, 18, 36
21. 11, 13, 17, 19 (red)
22. 18   23. 1 x 28
    2 x 9   2 x 14
    3 x 6   4 x 7
    1, 2, 3, 6, 9, 18   1, 2, 4, 7, 14, 28
24. 1, 3, 5, 15   25. 1, 2, 11, 22
26. 1, 2, 3, 5, 6, 10, 15, 30   27. 1, 2, 3, 6, 7, 14, 21, 42
28. 14, 7   29. 1, 2, 4, 7, 14, 28
30. 24, 12, 8, 6, 4   31. 30, 15, 10, 6, 5
    1, 2, 3, 4, 6, 8, 12, 24   1, 2, 3, 5, 6, 10, 15, 30
32. 1, 2, 4, 8   33. 1, 5, 7, 35
34. 1, 2, 3, 4, 6, 8, 12, 16, 24, 48
35. 1, 2, 3, 4, 5, 6, 10, 12, 15, 20, 30, 60

Activity

1. 16   2. 48   3. 14

13 More about Division

1.

$$1 \quad \xrightarrow{\text{2nd}} \quad 12 \quad \xrightarrow{\text{3rd}} \quad 124$$

$$2\overline{)248}$$

282 ÷ 2 = 124
124

2. 363 ÷ 3 = 121
   121
$$3\overline{)363}$$

3. 211   4. 213   5. 432
6. 111 r 3   7. 112 r 1   8. 344 r 1
9. 122 r 1   10. 111 r 2

11.
$$\begin{array}{r} 137 \\ 4\overline{)548} \\ 4 \\ \hline 14 \\ 12 \\ \hline 28 \\ 28 \end{array}$$

12.
$$\begin{array}{r} 89\,r\,3 \\ 4\overline{)359} \\ 32 \\ \hline 39 \\ 36 \\ \hline 3 \end{array}$$

13.
$$\begin{array}{r} 125\,r\,2 \\ 5\overline{)627} \\ 5 \\ \hline 12 \\ 10 \\ \hline 27 \\ 25 \\ \hline 2 \end{array}$$

14.
$$\begin{array}{r} 87\,r\,2 \\ 3\overline{)263} \\ 24 \\ \hline 23 \\ 21 \\ \hline 2 \end{array}$$

15.
$$\begin{array}{r} 131\,r\,3 \\ 4\overline{)527} \\ 4 \\ \hline 12 \\ 12 \\ \hline 7 \\ 4 \\ \hline 3 \end{array}$$

16.
$$\begin{array}{r} 99\,r\,5 \\ 6\overline{)599} \\ 54 \\ \hline 59 \\ 54 \\ \hline 5 \end{array}$$

17.
$$\begin{array}{r} 91\,r\,1 \\ 5\overline{)456} \\ 45 \\ \hline 6 \\ 5 \\ \hline 1 \end{array}$$

18.
$$\begin{array}{r} 155\,r\,2 \\ 3\overline{)467} \\ 3 \\ \hline 16 \\ 15 \\ \hline 17 \\ 15 \\ \hline 2 \end{array}$$

19.
$$\begin{array}{r} 122\,r\,2 \\ 7\overline{)856} \\ 7 \\ \hline 15 \\ 14 \\ \hline 16 \\ 14 \\ \hline 2 \end{array}$$

20.
$$\begin{array}{r} 93\,r\,5 \\ 9\overline{)842} \\ 81 \\ \hline 32 \\ 27 \\ \hline 5 \end{array}$$

21. 93 r 2   22. 64 r 2   23. 85 r 3
24. 68 r 2

25.
$$\begin{array}{r} 204 \\ 4\overline{)816} \\ 8 \\ \hline 16 \\ 16 \end{array}$$

26.
$$\begin{array}{r} 80 \\ 5\overline{)400} \\ 40 \\ \hline 0 \\ 0 \end{array}$$

27.
$$\begin{array}{r} 81 \\ 5\overline{)405} \\ 40 \\ \hline 5 \\ 5 \\ \hline 0 \end{array}$$

28.
$$\begin{array}{r} 81\,r\,4 \\ 5\overline{)409} \\ 40 \\ \hline 9 \\ 5 \\ \hline 4 \end{array}$$

29.
$$\begin{array}{r} 107 \\ 7\overline{)749} \\ 7 \\ \hline 49 \\ 49 \\ \hline 0 \end{array}$$

30.
$$\begin{array}{r} 127 \\ 4\overline{)508} \\ 4 \\ \hline 10 \\ 8 \\ \hline 28 \\ 28 \\ \hline 0 \end{array}$$

31.
$$\begin{array}{r} 206 \\ 3\overline{)618} \\ 6 \\ \hline 18 \\ 18 \\ \hline 0 \end{array}$$

32.
$$\begin{array}{r} 145 \\ 2\overline{)290} \\ 2 \\ \hline 9 \\ 8 \\ \hline 10 \\ 10 \\ \hline 0 \end{array}$$

33.
```
      104
5 ) 5 2 0
    5
    2 0
    2 0
        0
```

34.
```
      130
2 ) 2 6 0
    2
    6
    6
    0
    0
```

35.
```
      106
9 ) 9 5 4
    9
    5 4
    5 4
        0
        0
```

36.
```
      110
8 ) 8 8 0
    8
    8
    8
    0
    0
```

37.
```
      120
6 ) 7 2 0
    6
    1 2
    1 2
        0
        0
```

38.
```
      101 r 2
7 ) 7 0 9
    7
    9
    7
    2
```

39. 148 ÷ 4 = 37
37
```
      37
4 ) 1 4 8
    1 2
    2 8
    2 8
        0
```

40. 108 ÷ 9 = 12
12
```
      12
9 ) 1 0 8
    9
    1 8
    1 8
        0
```

41. 468 ÷ 6 = 78
78
```
      78
6 ) 4 6 8
    4 2
    4 8
    4 8
        0
```

42. 328 ÷ 8 = 41
41
```
      41
8 ) 3 2 8
    3 2
        8
        8
        0
```

Activity

C

14 Mixed Operations

1. 8 + 1 = 9
   9
2. 4 + 1 = 5
   5
3. 112, 76
4. 13, 72 (yellow)
5. 194 - 122 (yellow)
   72
6. 144 - 45
   99
7. 24 ÷ 3 = 8
   8
8. 5 x 5
   25
9. 164 ÷ 2
   82 (yellow)
10. 39 x 3
    117
11. 477 ÷ 3
    159
12. 27 x 6
    162 (yellow)
13. 123 x 4
    492 (yellow)

Activity

C (yellow)

15 Money

1. $5
2. $10
3. $50
4. $20
5. $100

6.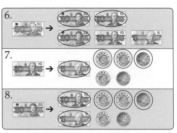

7.

8.

9. 61¢, $0.61   10. 51¢, $0.51   11. 28¢, $0.28

12. $20, $5, 50¢, 1¢   13. $25.51

14. Number of bills or coins: 1, 1, 1, 2
    Total: $10, $5, 25¢, 10¢

15. $15.35   16. $3.77, $2.23

17.
```
$ 0.95
+$ 1.07
$ 2.02
```
```
$ 5.00
-$ 2.02
$ 2.98
```

18.
```
$ 1.15
+$ 3.28
$ 4.43
```
```
$10.00
-$ 4.43
$ 5.57
```

19.
```
$ 1.23
$ 1.07
+$ 1.07
$ 3.37
```
```
$ 4.00
-$ 3.37
$ 0.63
```

20.
Total = $ 6.82

21.
Total = $ 6.34

22.
Total = $ 6.41

23.
Total = $ 7.38

Activity

1. I have 4 bills worth $40.
2. I have 4 bills worth $75.
3. I have 5 bills worth $100.

16 Fractions

1. $\frac{3}{10}$

2.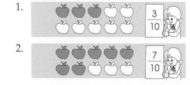
$\frac{7}{10}$

3.  $\frac{4}{9}$

4.  $\frac{5}{7}$

5. $\frac{2}{10}$ 6. $\frac{4}{10}$ 7. $\frac{5}{10}$

8. $\frac{4}{10}$ 9. $\frac{6}{10}$ 10. $\frac{7}{10}$

11. 4   12. 4   13. 6
14. 3   15. 6   16. 10
17. 2   18. A   19. C
20. B

21. $\frac{2}{8}$ 22. $\frac{2}{6}$, $\frac{3}{6}$ 23. $\frac{1}{2}+\frac{1}{2}=\frac{2}{2}$

24. $\frac{5}{7}$ 25. $\frac{8}{10}$ 26. $\frac{3}{5}$

27. $\frac{7}{8}$ 28. $\frac{5}{6}$ 29. $\frac{7}{7}$, 1

30. $\frac{9}{10}$ 31. $\frac{9}{9}$, 1   32. $\frac{4}{8}$

33. $\frac{3}{8}$, $\frac{4}{8}$ 34. $\frac{2}{12}$, $\frac{9}{12}$ 35. $\frac{2}{7}$

36. $\frac{3}{9}$ 37. $\frac{7}{11}$ 38. $\frac{1}{15}$

39. $\frac{6}{14}$ 40. $\frac{3}{16}$

Activity

1. $\frac{4}{8}$ 2. $\frac{2}{6}$

17 Capacity

1. C   2. B   3. F, A, B, C, E, D
4. 10 litres   5. 100 litres   6. 1 litre
7.   8.   9.

 2 L   3 L   8 L

10. 1
11. 4 - 2   12. 3 - 0
    2   3

Activity

1. 2   2. 5

18 Shapes

1. A.   B. C.

2.   3.   4.

5. B, D, F
6. D, E   7. B, C   8. A, F
9.   10.   11.

12. 6   13. 2   14. 0

19 Prisms and Pyramids

1. Triangular prism ☼
2. Rectangular prism ◎
3. Hexagonal prism ☆
4. Pentagonal prism ☺

5. A; Square   6. D; Hexagonal
7. E; Pentagonal   8. B; Triangular
9. C; Rectangular   10. 6; 12
11. 2; 1   12. 3; 2

Activity

1. A   2. C   3. D
4. B

20 Bar Graphs and Circle Graphs

1. 14   2. 10   3. 20
4. Green   5. 60
6.

The Number of Marbles Each Child Has

7. Peter   8. 3   9. George
10. George; 10   11. 90   12. 50
13. 260   14. 100   15. 50
16. 800   17. 150   18. Baseball
19. $\frac{1}{3}$ 20. Hockey   21. 4
22. 3   23. C   24. B
25. 11

Activity

A

21 Transformations and Grid

1. Flip   2. Slide   3. Flip
4. Turn

5. a. (4, 2) b. (5, 6) c. (6, 1)
6. B   7. C   8. 2, up; 3, left
9. 5, down; 2, right

Activity

1, 2.

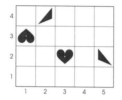

Final Test

1. 1 x 18
   2 x 9
   3 x 6
   1, 2, 3, 6, 9, 18

2. 1 x 20
   2 x 10
   4 x 5
   1, 2, 4, 5, 10, 20

3. 1 x 32
   2 x 16
   4 x 8
   1, 2, 4, 8, 16, 32

4. 1 x 45
   3 x 15
   5 x 9
   1, 3, 5, 9, 15, 45

5. 1, 2, 3, 4, 6, 9, 12, 18, 36

6. 1, 2, 3, 4, 6, 8, 12, 16, 24, 48

7.
```
     47
8) 376
   32
   56
   56
    0
```

8.
```
    152 r 1
5) 761
   5
   26
   25
   11
   10
    1
```

9.
```
    206 r 2
4) 826
   8
   26
   24
    2
```

10.
```
    89 r 8
9) 809
   72
   89
   81
    8
```

11.
```
    160 r 1
2) 321
   2
   12
   12
    1
    0
    1
```

12.
```
    202 r 1
3) 607
   6
   7
   6
   1
```

13.
```
    71 r 4
6) 430
   42
   10
    6
    4
```

14.
```
    48 r 6
7) 342
   28
   62
   56
    6
```

15.
```
    125 r 3
4) 503
   4
   10
    8
   23
   20
    3
```

16. [4 × 10 – 15] — [59 × 2 – 92]
17. [163 – 6 × 9] — [39 ÷ 3 + 12]
18. [70 ÷ 2 × 4] — [49 + 5 × 12]
19. [39 × 2 ÷ 3] — [116 – 8 × 7]
20. [135 ÷ 9 × 4] — [37 × 4 + 16]
21. [116 + 96 ÷ 2] — [120 ÷ 6 × 7]

22.
```
  $4.35
  $1.25
+ $0.99
  $6.59
```
```
  $6.75
- $6.59
  $0.16
```

23.
```
  $0.94
  $2.65
+ $1.07
  $4.66
```
```
  $6.00
- $4.66
  $1.34
```

24. D   25. B   26. A
27. C

28. $\dfrac{4}{12}$ 29. $\dfrac{5}{12}$ 30. $\dfrac{3}{12}$

31. $\dfrac{3}{12}$ 32. $\dfrac{8}{15}$ 33. $\dfrac{2}{4}$

34. $\dfrac{6}{7}$ 35. $\dfrac{2}{10}$ 36. $\dfrac{10}{10} = 1$

37. $\dfrac{2}{6}$ 38. $\dfrac{8}{8} = 1$

39.

40.

41.

42.

43. A, C, D   44. 1   45. 2
46. 0   47. 4   48. 0
49. 1
50.

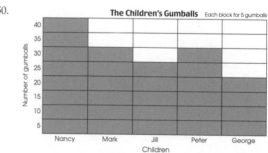

51. 30   52. Peter   53. Nancy
54. George; 5   55. 70   56. 145
57. 1, right; 2, up   58. 2, right; 1, down
59. 1, left; 1, up
60. a. B   b. A   c. C

Unit 1

1. Lesley, Gary Paul, Joe, Joan, Ann
2. 110, 100, 90, 80
3. Height : 145 – 130 = 15   Paul would have to grow 15 cm.
4. Difference : 145 – 120 = 25   The difference in height between the tallest student and the shortest student is 25 cm.
5. Paul, Joe, Lesley, Ann, Gary
6. No. of marbles : 513 – 100 = 413
   Lesley has 100 fewer marbles than Joe.
7. No. of marbles : 270 + 40 = 310
   Ann has 40 more marbles than Gary.
8. I will get to Ann's number first.
9. Joe can match Paul's score by winning 10 marbles.

Challenge

If Ann gives 10 to Gary, Ann will have 300 and Gary will have 280. ✗
If Ann gives 20 to Gary, Ann will have 290 and Gary will have 290. ✓
If Ann gives 20 marbles to Gary, they will have the same number of marbles.

Unit 2

1. There are 27 animals in all.
2. There are 15 4-legged animals.
3. No. of ducks : 15 + 9 = 24   There are 24 ducks altogether.
4. No. of animals : 3 + 9 = 12   There are 12 animals with wings.
5. No. of cows : 20 – 8 = 12   12 cows are still in the barn.
6. No. of animals : 15 – 12 = 3
   There are 3 more 4-legged animals than 2-legged ones.
7. He should buy : 64 – 39 = 25   He should buy 25 more goats.
8. No. of animals : 68 + 23 = 91   He has 91 animals now.
9. No. of birds : 24 + 34 + 59 = 117   He has 117 birds.
10. Peter sold : 47 + 59 = 106   Peter sold 106 cows and goats altogether.
11. No. of gulls : 196 – 98 + 105 = 203   There are 203 gulls altogether.
12. No. of gulls : 312 + 64 = 376   There were 376 gulls at the start.
13. No. of gulls : 305 – 84 = 221   221 gulls are left.
14. No. of gulls : 576 – 153 – 283 = 140   140 gulls remain.
15. No. of gulls : 413 + 311 + 136 = 860   There are 860 gulls altogether.
16. ducks   17. cows   18. chickens
19. goats   20. sheep   21. pigs
22. He should use field B because 48 is closer to 50.
23. No. of trees : 150 – 68 = 82
    He can plant 82 more trees there afterwards.
24. No. of trees : (25 + 50) – 68 = 7
    He can plant 7 more trees there afterwards.
25. No. of trees : 53 + 75 = 128
    He should choose field C because it can hold more than 100 trees.
26. No. of trees : 150 – 128 = 22   He can plant 22 more trees there.
27. No. of peach trees : 91 – 36 = 55
    No. of trees : 100 – 55 = 45   He can plant 45 more trees.

Challenge

No. of ducks	No. of sheep	No. of legs	
1	8	2 + 32 = 34	✗
2	7	4 + 28 = 32	✓

There are 2 ducks and 7 sheep.

Unit 3

1.	⚅⚅⚅⚅⚅	5 x 4	20
2.	⚅⚅⚅⚅⚅	5 x 6	30
3.	⚅⚅⚅	3 x 4	12
4.	⚅⚅⚅⚅	4 x 7	28
5.	⚅⚅⚅	3 x 5	15
6.	⚅⚅⚅⚅⚅⚅	6 x 2	12

7. 5 plates with 3 apples each. 5 x 3 = 15
   There are 15 apples in all.
8. 6 plates with 4 oranges each. 6 x 4 = 24
   There are 24 oranges in all.
9. 7 baskets with 2 pears each. 7 x 2 = 14
   There are 14 pears in all.
10. 6 bags with 1 watermelon each. 6 x 1 = 6
    There are 6 watermelons in all.
11. 3 plates with 8 cherries each. 3 x 8 = 24
    There are 24 cherries in all.
12. 6 x 8 = 48   There are 48 apples.
13. 9 x 7 = 63   There are 63 oranges.
14. 5 x 3 = 15   3 children will get 15 candies in all.
15. 7 x 4 = 28   4 children will get 28 crackers in all.
16. 5 x 5 = 25   5 children will get 25 chicken nuggets in all.
17. 6 x 5 = 30   5 children will get 30 cookies in all.
18. 2 x 7 = 14   7 children will get 14 cheese sticks in all.
19. 3 x 2 = 6   2 children will get 6 brownies in all.
20. 8 x 6 = 48   6 children will get 48 marshmallows in all.
21. 4 x 4 = 16   4 children will get 16 pretzels in all.
22. 6 x 6 = 36   There are 36 chips.
23. 2 x 7 = 14   There are 14 pieces of cheese.
24. 5 x 8 = 40   There are 40 grams of marshmallows.
25. 6 x 5 = 30   A plate of candies costs 30¢.

Challenge

He saved : 10 + 20 + 30 = 60   Terry saved 60¢ altogether.

Unit 4

1.
   10 ÷ 5 = 2
   Each child will get 2 cupcakes.

2.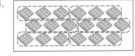
   12 ÷ 3 = 4
   Each boy will get 4 cookies.

3.
   20 ÷ 5 = 4
   There are 4 candies in each group.

4.
   18 ÷ 6 = 3
   Each child will get 3 crackers.

5. 24 ÷ 3 = 8 She needs 8 baskets. 6. 24 ÷ 4 = 6 She needs 6 baskets.
7. 24 ÷ 6 = 4 She needs 4 baskets. 8. 24 ÷ 8 = 3 She needs 3 baskets.
9. No. of chocolate doughnuts : 8 ÷ 2 = 4
   There are 4 chocolate doughnuts in each group.
10. No. of honey doughnuts : 16 ÷ 2 = 8
    There are 8 honey doughnuts in each group.
11. No. of chocolate doughnuts : 8 ÷ 4 = 2
    No. of honey doughnuts : 16 ÷ 4 = 4
    There are 2 chocolate doughnuts and 4 honey doughnuts in each group.
12. 24 ÷ 5 = 4...4
    There are 4 groups, and 4 students are left over.
13. 30 ÷ 4 = 7...2
    Each student can get 7 crayons, and 2 crayons are left over.
14. 48 ÷ 9 = 5...3
    Each student can get 5 markers, and 3 markers are left over.
15. 61 ÷ 7 = 8...5
    Each student can get 8 markers, and 5 markers are left over.
16. There are 6 pencils. If each student gets 2 pencils, Mrs Winter can give them to 3 students.
17. There are 7 glue sticks. If each student gets 1 glue stick, Mrs Winter can give them to 7 students.

18. No. of erasers : 19 − 7 x 2 = 19 − 14 = 5
    5 erasers are left over; no glue sticks are left over.
19. 36 ÷ 4 = 9   He would need 9 small boxes.
20. 36 ÷ 6 = 6   He would need 6 big boxes.
21. 48 ÷ 4 = 12   He would need 12 small boxes.
22. 18 ÷ 4 = 4...2   He would need 5 small boxes.
23. 26 ÷ 4 = 6...2   He would need 7 small boxes.
24. 26 ÷ 6 = 4...2   He would need 5 big boxes.

Challenge

1. No. of boxes : 12 ÷ 4 = 3   I paid : 3 x 3 = 9
   I would buy 3 small boxes and pay $9.
2. No. of boxes : 12 ÷ 6 = 2   I paid : 2 x 4 = 8
   I would buy 2 big boxes and pay $8.
3. The big box is a better deal. It costs less to buy 12 cupcakes in big boxes.

Unit 5

1. 3; 3; $\frac{2}{3}$ 2. 8; 8; $\frac{5}{8}$ 3. 6; 6; $\frac{3}{6}$

4. $\frac{6}{16}$ of the groceries are bags.   5. $\frac{10}{16}$ of the groceries are cans.
6. $\frac{3}{16}$ of the groceries are 🛍.   7. $\frac{4}{16}$ of the groceries are 🥫.
8. $\frac{3}{16}$ of the groceries are 👜.   9. $\frac{6}{16}$ of the groceries are 🥫.

10.

No. of groceries in bags	6	7	8	9	10
No. of groceries	16	17	18	19	20

She would need 4 more bags.

11.

No. of groceries in cans	10	9	8	7	6
No. of groceries	16	15	14	13	12

She would take away 4 cans.

12. $\frac{4}{6}$ of the beads are yellow.   13. $\frac{2}{6}$ of the beads are red.

14.

● Yellow
○ Red

15. $\frac{6}{12}$ of the beads are red.   16. $\frac{2}{12}$ of the beads are yellow.
17. $\frac{3}{12}$ of the beads are blue.   18. $\frac{1}{12}$ of the beads are orange.

19.

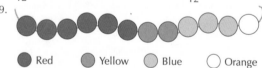

● Red   ● Yellow   ○ Blue   ○ Orange

20. $\frac{11}{20}$ of the drinks are pop.
21. $\frac{9}{20}$ of the drinks are juice.
22. $\frac{4}{9}$ of the juices are orange flavour.
23. $\frac{8}{11}$ of the pops are orange flavour.
24. $\frac{8}{20}$ of the drinks are grape flavour.
25. $\frac{12}{20}$ of the drinks are orange flavour.

Challenge

1. $\frac{1}{3}$ 2. $\frac{1}{4}$ 3. $\frac{1}{5}$

Unit 6

1. Joe used 1 quarter and 1 nickel.
2. Katherine used 1 twoonie and 3 pennies.

3. William used 1 twoonie, 1 loonie, 1 dime and 1 nickel.
4. Ann used 1 loonie, 3 quarters, 1 nickel and 1 penny.
5. Cost : 2.20 + 2.20 = 4.40
   Natasha used 2 twoonies, 1 quarter, 1 dime and 1 nickel.
6. Cost : 1.86 + 1.28 = 3.14   Jane needs to pay $3.14.
7. Cost : 1.68 + 0.95 = 2.63   They cost $2.63.
8. Cost : 2.75 + 2.75 + 1.86 = 7.36   Susan needs to pay $7.36.
9. Change : 10.00 − 1.68 − 1.28 = 7.04   Tom got $7.04 change.
10. If Daisy bought fries, she would have $0.95 (1.99 − 1.04 = 0.95) left. Pop costs $0.95. Daisy bought fries and pop.
11. Cost for 3 fries : 1.04 + 1.04 + 1.04 = 3.12 > 3.1 (Money Nicky has)
    No. It is not enough for 3 fries.
12. Change : 10 − 7.5 = 2.5   Joan's change was $2.50.
    The coins are 1 twoonie and 2 quarters.
13. Change : 7 − 5.75 = 1.25   David's change was $1.25.
    The coins are 1 loonie and 1 quarter.
14. Change : 10 − 4.25 − 4.25 = 1.5   Raymond's change was $1.50.
    The coins are 1 loonie and 2 quarters.
15. Change : 5 − 1.85 − 1.85 = 1.3   Lily's change was $1.30.
    The coins are 1 loonie, 1 quarter and 1 nickel.
16. Change : 10 − 1.38 − 1.85 − 5.75 = 1.02
    Daisy's change was $1.02.   The coins are 1 loonie and 2 pennies.
17. 5.00   18. 2.00   19. 11.00   20. 10.76
21. 1.00   22. 6.00   23. 3.00   24. 2.00
25. 12.00   26. 12.91   27. 3.00   28. 5.00
29. 3.00   30. 1.00   31. 12.00   32. 12.47

Challenge

Jessie's change   Wendy's change   Brian's change
20 − 10.76 = 9.24   15 − 12.91 = 2.09   13 − 12.47 = 0.53
Jessie would get the most change back.

Midway Review

1. $3.30, $2.70, $2.50, $1.75, $1.50
2. Change : 2 − 0.8 − 0.8 = 0.4   She will get $0.40 (40¢) change.
3. Change : 5 − 0.8 − 0.8 = 3.4   B would be the change.
4. 🪙🪙🪙🪙🪙🪙🪙🪙🪙🪙   She can get 10 quarters.
5. No. of quarters : 10 ÷ 5 = 2; Value : 0.25 + 0.25 = 0.5
   Each group has 2 quarters and its value is $0.50 (50¢).
6. (1 week; $0.75) ⟶ (2 weeks; $1.50) ⟶ (3 weeks; $2.25)
   She will take 3 weeks to earn $2.25.
7. Ann has 13 marbles.
8. No. of marbles : 13 + 29 = 42   She will have 42 marbles altogether.
9. $\frac{5}{13}$ of marbles are black.
10. $\frac{4}{13}$ of marbles have a cat's eye.
11. No. of marbles : 13 − 8 = 5   She would have 5 marbles.
12.

No. of marbles in black	5	6	7	8
No. of marbles in all	13	14	15	16

Ann would have to buy 3 black marbles.

13. No. of marbles : 13 ÷ 3 = 4...1
    Each child will get 4 marbles and 1 marble will be left over.
14. Cost : 3 x 6 = 18   They cost $18.00 in all.
15. She spent : 24 ÷ 6 = 4   She spent $4.00 on each mouse.
16. No. of baby mice : 4 x 2 − 2 = 6   6 baby mice were left.
17. Amount : 5 x 5 = 25   She will get $25.00.
18. No. of mice : 40 ÷ 5 = 8   She would need to sell 8 mice.
19. Ball, ladder, tunnel : 3.25 + 1.75 + 2 = 7
    She should choose a ball, a ladder and a tunnel.
20. Change : 9 − 3.25 − 4.25 = 1.5   She would get $1.50 change.
21. B   22. D   23. B   24. A
25. B   26. A   27. C   28. B

Unit 7

1. Capacity : 1 x 4 = 4   The capacity is 4 L.
2. Capacity : 1 x 5 = 5   5 jugs can hold 5 L of water.
3. Capacity : 4 x 3 = 12   12 L of water can fill 3 buckets.
4. Capacity : 1 + 4 = 5   5 L of water can fill 1jug and 1 bucket.
5. 2 jugs hold : 1000 x 2 = 2000   2 jugs hold 2000 millilitres of water.
6. 2 buckets : 8 L   5 jugs : 5 L   2 buckets hold more.
7. No. of jugs : 4 x 3 = 12   She can fill 12 jugs.
8. 2.5 L   9. 1 L   10. 5 L
11. Capacity : 2.5 + 2.5 = 5   2 vases can hold 5 L of water.
12. Capacity : 1 + 1 + 1 + 1 = 4   4 bottles can hold 4 L of water.
13. Capacity : 5 + 5 = 10   2 pots can hold 10 L of water.
14.

No. of vases	1	2	3	4
Capacity	2.5	5	7.5	10

4 vases are needed.
15. No. of pots : 20 ÷ 5 = 4   4 pots are needed.
16. The pot has the greatest capacity.
17. Difference : 5 – 2.5 = 2.5
   A pot can hold 2.5 L more water than a vase.
18. Difference : 3 – 2.5 = 0.5
   3 bottles can hold 0.5 L more water than a vase.
19. A pot can hold 5 L; a vase can hold 2.5 L.
   A pot can hold 2 times more water than a vase.
20. Water a vase can hold : 1000 + 1000 + 500 = 2500
   A vase can hold 2500 millilitres of water.
21. C   22. M   23. C   24. M
25. Mass : (1000 + 1000 + 1000) ÷ 2 = 1500
   The mass of a story book is 1500 g (1.5 kg).
26. Mass : 100 + 200 + 200 = 500
   The mass of an exercise book is 500 g.
27. Difference : 1500 – 500 = 1000
   A story book is 1000 g heavier than an exercise book.
28. (1 exercise book; 500 g) ⟶ (2 exercise books; 1000 g) ⟶
   (3 exercise books; 1500 g)
   3 exercise books will have about the same mass as a story book.
29. A strawberry is lighter than a banana.
30. A watermelon is heavier than a pineapple.
31. An apple is heavier than a banana but lighter than an orange.
32. Watermelon, pineapple, orange, apple, banana, strawberry.

Challenge

1.

No. of oranges	3	6	9	12
Orange juice	250mL	500mL	750mL	1000mL

She needs 12 oranges.

2. (3 oranges; 1 kg) ⟶ (12 oranges; 4 kg)   She needs 4 kg of oranges.

Unit 8

1. Pencil E is the longest.
2. Pencil B is the shortest.
3. Difference : 8 – 5 = 3   Pencil C is 3 cm longer than Pencil A.
4. Difference : 15 – 3 = 12   Pencil B is 12 cm shorter than Pencil E.
5.
   5 cm —after 1 week→ 4 cm —after 1 week→ 3 cm

   It will take 2 weeks.
6. No. of weeks : 15 – 8 = 7   It will take 7 weeks.
7. Length : 12 – 7 = 5   It will be 5 cm long.
8. 12; 8; 9; 12; 16; 13
9. Shape E has the greatest perimeter.
10. Shape B has the smallest perimeter.
11. Shape A and shape D have the same perimeter.
12. Difference : 13 – 9 = 4
   The perimeter of F is 4 cm greater than that of C.
13. Times : 16 ÷ 8 = 2   The perimeter of E is 2 times greater than that of B.

14. F has a greater perimeter than A, but smaller than E.
15. 10; 10; 9; 8; 12
16. Sticker E has the greatest area.
17. Sticker D has the smallest area.
18. Difference : 12 – 9 = 3
   The area of sticker C is 3 cm² smaller than that of sticker E.
19. Difference : 10 – 8 = 2
   The area of sticker B is 2cm² greater than that of sticker D.
20. C has a greater area than that of D, but smaller than that of A.
21. 2 A stickers are needed.   22. Shape B has the greatest area.
23. Shape C has the greatest perimeter.
24. Shape C and shape E have the same area.
25. Shape B and shape E have the same perimeter.
26. Difference : 7 – 3 = 4   The area of B is 4 cm² greater than that of A.
27. Difference : 14 – 10 = 4
   The perimeter of D is 4 cm smaller than that of C.

Challenge

Perimeter : (2 + 6) x 2 + (9 + 2) x 2 – (6 + 9) x 2 = 8
The new perimeter is 8 cm greater than the old perimeter.

Unit 9

1. 4 flowers are in a pattern.   2.
3.   4.
5. 3 flowers are in the pattern.   6. 🌷🌷🌷
7. 🌷 is the second.   8. 🌷 is the first.
9. It grows 5 cm every week.
10. Height : 20 + 5 + 5 = 30   The height will be 30 cm.
11. It grows 2 cm every week.
12. Height : 8 + 2 + 2 = 12   The height will be 12 cm.
13. It grows 4 cm every week.
14. Height : 16 + 4 + 4 = 24   The height will be 24 cm.
15.

Week	4	5	6	7
Height (cm)	20	25	30	35

It will take 7 weeks.

16.

Week	4	5	6
Height (cm)	8	10	12

It will take 6 weeks.

17.

Week	4	5	6	7
Height (cm)	16	20	24	28

It will take 7 weeks.

18.   19.   20.

21. 10; 12; 14; 16; 18
22. [8th] [9th] [10th]
   18 ⟶ 20 ⟶ 22   22 blocks are used.
23. 16; 25; 36; 49; 64
24. [8th] [9th] [10th]
   64 ⟶ 81 ⟶ 100   100 blocks are used.
25. 10; 15; 21; 28; 36
26. [8th] [9th] [10th]
   36 ⟶ 45 ⟶ 55   55 blocks are used.
27. The numbers get bigger by 5.
28. The next 4 numbers are 35, 40, 45 and 50.
29. The numbers get smaller by 10.
30. The next 4 numbers are 60, 50, 40 and 30.
31. The numbers get bigger by 2.
32. The next 4 numbers are 266, 268, 270 and 272.
33. The numbers get smaller by 100.
34. The next 4 numbers are 419, 319, 219 and 119.

Challenge

1.

Day	1	2	3	4	5	6
Saved ¢	12	24	36	48	60	72

Joan has saved 72¢ ($0.72) on the 6th day.

2.

Day	6	7	8	9	10
Saved ¢	72	84	96	108	120

Joan will take 10 days to have 120¢ ($1.20).

Unit 10

1. A : Rectangular pyramid   B : Cylinder
   C : Cube   D : Triangular prism
   E : Cone   F : Sphere
2. A has 5 faces.   3. C has 6 faces.
4. B has 2 circular faces.   5. B, C and D can be stacked.
6. B, E and F can roll.
7. A : Square   B : Rectangle
   C : Circle   D : Pentagon
   E : Triangle   F : Hexagon
   G : Parallelogram   H : Trapezoid
8. E has 3 sides.   9. A, B, G and H have 4 sides.
10. A has 4 equal sides.   11. F has 6 vertices.
12. There are 4 lines of symmetry. 13. There are 2 lines of symmetry.
14. C is the top view of a cylinder. 15. E is its top view.
16. ⊤   17. ⌐
18. 1 square up and 5 squares to the right.
19. 3 squares down and 2 squares to the right.
20. 3 squares down and 5 squares to the right.
21. 3 squares down.   22. 3 squares to the left.
23. 1 square down and 6 squares to the right.
24. 1 square up and 7 squares to the right.
25. 2 squares down and 6 squares to the right.
26. ⬡ , ⊤ and ∨ are symmetrical.
27. It has 2 lines of symmetry. 28. It has 1 line of symmetry.
29. It has 1 line of symmetry. 30. It is similar to ⬡ .
31. It is congruent to ⊥ . 32. It is congruent to ⌐ .

Challenge

1. No. of sides of a triangle and a square : 3 + 4 = 7
   No. of each shape : 21 ÷ 7 = 3   Jill has 3 triangles and 3 squares.
2. A circle has many lines of symmetry.

Unit 11

1. No. of cars : 8 x 2 = 16   16 cars were parked there.
2. Difference : 16 – 8 = 8   There were 8 more cars than vans.
3. No. of vehicles : 18 x 2 = 36   There were 36 vehicles.
4. No. of people : 8 x 3 = 24
   24 people came to the pizza store by van.
5. Number of pizzas ordered.   6. There are 3 sizes.
7. It stands for 1 order.
8. No. of pizzas : 6 x 2 = 12   12 small pizzas were ordered.
9. Difference : 18 – 9 = 9
   9 more medium pizzas were ordered than large pizzas.
10. No. of pizzas : 12 + 18 + 9 = 39   39 pizzas were ordered in all.

Challenge

Pepperoni	◐ ◐ ◐ ◐ ◐
Vegetarian	◐ ◐ ◐ ◐ ◐
Hawaiian	◐ ◐ ◐ ◐ ◐

Unit 12

1. Customers' choice of one-topping pizzas.

2. 10 people chose bacon.   3. 8 people chose pineapple.
4. Difference : 14 – 8 = 6
   6 more people chose mushroom than pineapple.
5. No. of people : 10 + 12 = 22   22 people preferred meat.
6. No. of pizzas : 14 + 10 + 8 + 12 = 44
   44 pizzas were ordered in all.
7.

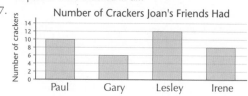

Number of Crackers Joan's Friends Had

8. Gary had 6 crackers.
9. Difference : 12 – 8 = 4   Lesley had 4 more crackers than Irene.
10. Lesley had more crackers than Paul.
11. No. of crackers : 10 + 6 + 12 + 8 = 36
    The children had 36 crackers in all.

Challenge

Gary had 6 crackers and Irene had 8 crackers, so Joan had 7 crackers.

Final Review

1. 2   2. 4   3. 6   4. 8   5. 10
6. The lengths of the pencils increase by 2 cm.
7. Their lengths would be 12 cm and 14 cm.
8. Perimeter : 15 + 5 + 15 + 5 = 40   Area : 75
   Its perimeter is 40 cm and its area is 75 cm².
9. A   10. A   11. A   12. B
13. It is a cylinder. It has 3 faces.
14. It is a triangular prism. It has 5 faces.
15. It is a cube. It has 6 faces.
16. John bought gift B for Ann.   17. Katie bought gift C for Ann.
18. Capacity : 500 x 6 = 3000   The capacity of a jug is 3000 mL (3 L).
19. Capacity : 500 x 8 = 4000   The capacity of a vase is 4000 mL (4 L).
20. There are 1000 millilitres in a litre.
21. A glass has a capacity of less than 1 L.
22. A jug can fill 6 cups; a bottle can fill 3 cups. The capacity of a jug
    is 2 times more than that of a bottle.
23. A bottle can hold 1500 mL. Two bottles can hold 3000 mL.
    2 bottles are needed to hold 3 L of juice.
24. 2 bottles can hold 3 L; 5 glasses can hold 2.5 L. 2 bottles hold more.
25. Capacity : 3 + 3 = 6   The capacity of a bucket is 6 L.
26. 2 cups can fill a bowl. The capacity of a bowl is 1 L.
27.

Number of Glasses of Water the Children Drank Last Week

28. Difference : 55 – 40 = 15
    George drank 15 more glasses of water than David.
29. No. of bottles : 60 ÷ 6 = 10   Katie drank 10 bottles of water.
30. No. of glasses : 50 + 45 + 60 + 55 + 40 = 250
    The children drank 250 glasses of water in all.
31. Joan drank $\frac{50}{250}$ of the total number of glasses of water.
32. There are 3 triangles.   33. ◯   34. ▢
35. 2 blocks up and 3 blocks to the left.
36. 2 blocks down and 1 block to the right.
37. Joan used a triangular prism.
38. 1 block up and 2 blocks to the right.
39. 5 blocks to the right.
40. 2 blocks up and 6 blocks to the right.